40

sex and the nature of things

N. J. BERRILL

WITH DRAWINGS BY THE AUTHOR

DODD, MEAD & COMPANY · NEW YORK · 1954

FOREWORD OR FOREWARNED

This book is written for those who have some interest in sex and the nature of things but who are
otherwise not biologically informed. If any biologist should read it, he should know that he is lis-
tening in on a private conversation in which the
technical language of genetics and hormone chemistry is definitely out of place.

To one man's family

Library of Congress Catalog Card Number: 53-10254

introduction

Some time ago a book was written called *Is Sex Necessary?* It is a title that lingers in the mind, for the question it poses is one that leads to further questions, and when you follow these in turn there seems to be no end. Is sex necessary for what? There is no simple answer, for the roots of sex go deep into the very nature of things, and we are the products of sex in more ways than one.

When I first thought I would write this book it seemed a fairly simple matter, a straightforward one, at least. Yet, as so often happens, any door that opens onto the living world is just an entrance like any other; before you know it you are far into the realm of nature as a whole. It was my intention to make a survey of sex throughout the living kingdom—and I hope I will have done this at least—but one thing, as always, leads to another and it becomes difficult to draw a line. Putting limits to a discussion is an arbitrary action at the best, and when the subject leads to the heart of life itself, limitation becomes absurd and is something dictated by incidental things: the reader's interest span perhaps; or my own ability to reflect within the constrictions of writing the realities of the natural world, without getting lost in its maze of detail; or by the length that a book should be, which is a question of economics. All of these have their say. They restrict inquiry and contemplation to what may seem to be expedient.

At first it seemed that the obvious thing to do in this book was to abstract sex from nature and portray the story of its variant form, of how it has changed throughout the course of time, and also to present sex as something with a reality all its own. All this can be done in part; yet the mirror you hold up does not fully reflect the truth, but only one color of it, and thus the impression it makes is misleading. For only in the totality of life, present and past, does sex find its proper setting—and in that setting it loses neither significance nor importance, but gains in stature greatly. It was Aristotle, I think, who said there is no such thing as hot water, but only hot water in some container. Sex also makes sense only in relation to other things—to the organisms that express it, to the environment they live in and to their long and changing past as organisms in a changing world. Consequently throughout this book, or most of it, sex becomes part of the nature of things and does not stand alone; how much a part, it has startled me to discover. For sex is the basis of evolution. Reproduction by itself is something else, although the two have become so thoroughly entangled they must be taken together.

Whenever we look upon man as an animal, an element of self-consciousness intrudes, and it is a little difficult to get the right degree of detachment. We look into the mirror and see more perhaps than we expected: not only ourselves but all of life stretching across the field and backward into time. It is not easy to comprehend what it is we see, for the pattern is complex and full of meaning; and we have been peering for so long into the murky glass that our imagination has run riot. We think we see more clearly now but it is only a relative clarity, and so recently has it come that we are still inclined to mix fable with fact and to underestimate our ignorance.

To get the setting, we need to start with the beginning of things from our purely human point of view, how men have looked upon their own existence and the problem of their origin throughout the ages—the slow polishing of the mirror, if we keep to that analogy. And we will finish with an objective study of man, which in a sense closes the circle. You can start if you like with the end and work backward, or read the first and last chapters together and fill in between—such is your privilege, for you are human with the dominant human point of view. Yet I am a biologist as well, with a greater concern for the so-called lesser forms of life; and so in between man at the start and at the finish, I intend to wander where I find my interest takes me. For throughout and everywhere there is a pageant of evolving life of which man is a part but not the focus, and the whole has greater meaning than any particular piece of it, no matter what the piece may be.

contents

PART ONE

PART ONE

SEX AND THE NATURE OF THINGS

1. the light dawns

What primitive men thought about themselves and how they came to be we can only guess from the few signs and symbols they have left inscribed in various places; also from what the more isolated primitive peoples of our present world still believe, or have believed, at least, until their isolated innocence was tampered with; and still more from legends and myths that have come down to us in our own folklore and perhaps in our religion. We have no right to feel superior to these early men, for we build on their past— our brains have not improved in a hundred thousand years. What has developed is communication, the passing on of experience and insight from one generation to the next.

Children discover how they are conceived and born only by instruction of one kind or another. Sexual instinct may come naturally, but not understanding—and the truth that a child is born only in consequence of an act of sexual union, is in fact the result of such an act, is still imperfectly realized, even unsuspected, by certain primitive races in the world today.

Early man faced the unknown to a far greater degree than we, and as long as no connection was made between the act of mating and the production of offspring, in either man or

3

beast, it is not surprising to find fantastic and startling ideas prevailing concerning the origin of newborn life. Since time out of mind we have tried to find answers to the problems that plague us, and most of the answers have been strange indeed.

It is almost impossible to put oneself back into the state of ignorance and confusion either of a very young child or of early humanity, although the effort I think would be more entertaining and more effective on a sleepless night than counting sheep. Some idea, however, of the kind of things we all once thought can still be found among the more isolated tribes of Australian aborigines.

I suppose the topic of the chicken and the egg has always been with us—that birds lay eggs and that nestlings hatch out of them could hardly have been overlooked at any time. But the eggs of other animals for the most part have been too small to see; while the commencement of human life, and that of other mammals, has been one of the great mysteries that have vexed us throughout our history.

The events of conception and development not only take place deep within the female body, but the act of sexual union and the first signs that offspring are developing have been difficult to associate, since too great an interval of time lies in between. At first I suppose men measured time only from sunrise to sunrise, and it required a very long step forward to reckon by the waxing and waning of the moon. Mating between man and woman might produce a child, but just as likely it did not—and certain races to this day do not associate the two events. Aboriginal Australians date conception from the time a woman first becomes aware of the quickening within her; in Borneo, among certain tribes, only seeing is believing, and the swelling is the start of things.

4

Pregnancy becomes a mystery ascribed to supernatural powers. One eastern Australian tribe believes girl babies to be fashioned by the moon, boys by the wood lizard—and there is a traditional English rhyme about what boys and girls are made of which may be a relic from an ignorant past. In Queensland the thundergod makes babies out of swamp mud and inserts them into the womb; or a woman conceives because she has been sitting over a fire on which she has roasted a particular kind of fish, or because she has hunted and caught a certain kind of frog; or a man other than her mate has ordered the ghost of a dying kangaroo to go to her. The spirit children are no larger than a sand grain, and enter the womb through the navel.

Other races have been no less imaginative, and all in one way or another have attempted to solve the riddle. In the pueblos of New Mexico the people thought that a maid conceived from a heavy summer shower and bore Montezuma; the Greek goddess Aphrodite was born from the foam of the sea; the Celtic saint Maedoc was born of a star which fell into his mother's mouth while she slept; the founder of the Manchu dynasty was born to a maiden because she ate red fruit placed on her skirt by a magpie; while the red pomegranate placed by the nymph Nana in her bosom brought forth Attis. Virgin births have been commonplace. Why not, when no man was thought to be responsible? Even the wind has been potent: the Indian maiden, called Wenonah in Longfellow's poem, was quickened by the West Wind and bore Michabo, the Algonquin hero we know as Hiawatha; and in Germany in the spring, when the wind waved through the fields of wheat, the peasants said "there comes the Corn mother"—the wind, personified and fertile. And going back to another root, the Druids believed that the power

5

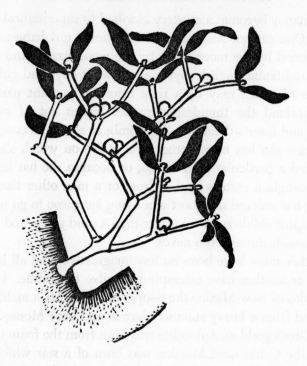

of the mistletoe made women fruitful. Kissing under the mistletoe comes from the pagan rites and it takes but a little thought to see how the plant and pregnancy may have acquired association in the mind. And there is the ever present magic of fire light—it fascinates, no matter how sophisticated you are. Leaping over bonfires is an old and widespread custom supposed to promote marriage and to procure offspring for childless couples—not that the fire itself has been the fertilizing energy, but it was thought to have the power to remove obstacles which the spells of witches and wizards put in the way of man and wife. We know a little better now, it is true, but a fireside is a potent place. It has cradled

6

our dawning humanity in so many ways—it will be a pity if we lose it.

Man was a hunter for more than one half a million years before he domesticated animals and settled down more or less to plant and tend his crops. And wherever crops were grown and human settlements developed, the seasons of sowing and harvesting, fertility and ripening, took hold of the imagination. Male and female were qualities not only of men and women but of all things—the sun and the moon, of trees and flowers—and sexual union, pregnancy, the fertility of plants and animals alike, were all comingled and confused.

Trees became animate in the minds of men. The tree soul became a forest god able to make the crops grow, the sun shine, the rain fall, to make flocks and herds multiply and cause women to bring forth more easily. And what worked one way could work the other. Our ancestors of not so long ago attempted to quicken the growth of trees and other plants, on the principle of imitative magic, by representing the marriage of the woodland gods in the person of the king and queen of May or a Whitsun bridegroom and bride. Only the more innocent part of these ceremonies now survives, but in pagan times when the ritual was conducted in deadly earnest, symbolic marriage was not enough, and promiscuous intercourse among otherwise monogamous men and women was the order of the day. This was far from being unbridled lust, but a ceremony purposely and solemnly organized to promote the fertility of the earth and its dependent human welfare.

At different times in different places, religions replace the older magic. In the form of Osiris, Tammuz, Adonis and Attis, the races of Egypt and western Asia represented the

7

decay and revival of life, particularly of vegetation, as per-
sonification in the form of a god who annually dies and
comes to life again.

In the days of Babylon, Tammuz appears as the youthful
lover of Ishtar, the great goddess of reproduction. Every
year Tammuz was supposed to die, passing from the cheer-
ful earth to the darker netherworld, and every year his
divine mistress went in quest of him. During her absence
the passion of love ceased to operate, and men and beasts
alike forgot to reproduce their kind, so that all life was
threatened with extinction. Thus the seasons reflected the
presence and absence of the goddess, and without her the
sexual and reproductive functions of the whole living world
could not be performed.

Tammuz was worshiped by the Semitic people of both
Babylonia and Syria, but as early as 600 B.C. the Greeks bor-
rowed him, mistook his title for his name and called him
Adonis. He became the handsome youth beloved by Aphrodite, the goddess of love, and also by Persephone, queen of
the underworld. The rivalry was resolved by Zeus himself,
who decreed that Adonis should abide with Persephone for
part of the year and with Aphrodite for the other part, the
seasons of winter and death and summer fruitfulness—a
recognition of the breeding seasons, though linked to a
supernatural being.

Another Semitic race had this to say, in words inscribed
during the ninth century B.C., in the land of Canaan: "And
God said unto Noah, . . . 'of every living thing of all flesh,
two of every sort shall thou bring into the ark, to keep them
alive with thee; they shall be male and female. Of fowls
after their kind, and of cattle after their kind, of every creeping thing of the earth after his kind, two of every sort shall

8

come unto thee, to keep them alive . . . to keep seed alive upon the face of the earth.'" And there it is—the fitting of the sexes into the scheme of things.

In all of this there is a dawning insight into the nature of things, of the meaning of sex and reproduction, but understanding has been slow to come, has advanced by fits and starts and has been hard to hold on to.

For knowledge can be lost as well as gained, and ignorance and superstition often flourish alongside understanding. Knowledge can be ancient as well as new. There are prescriptions for contraception, abortion and for obtaining permanent sterility in an Egyptian papyrus of the Twelfth Dynasty—2500 to 3000 B.C., and somewhat similar instructions in another dated about 1500 B.C. In the sacred books of India, of about 600 B.C., the origin of living things is divided into three classes: "that which springs from an egg, that which springs from a living being, and that which springs from a germ." The Hindu writers also held that conception comes from the union of semen and menstrual blood —one of the oldest ideas and one that was also held by the Greeks; it followed from the observation that menstruation is interrupted by pregnancy. The soul entered the body in the seventh month, the age at which a prematurely born child first has a chance to live; although according to Aristotle, in the fourth century B.C., only the highly sensitive soul did so. The ovary had no part at all to play.

As for sex, said the Greeks, males were generated in the left-hand side of the womb, females in the right. Again according to Aristotle, heat and cold were the causes of male and female sex in such creatures as fish and serpents, while in humans more males were born if sexual union occurred when the north winds rather than the south were blowing. Yet it was Aristotle himself who said—"he who sees things from their beginnings will have the finest view of them."

After a few later flickers the Greek flame went out and there is nothing to tell for two thousand years. All the freshness of knowledge disappears, what is left becomes distorted and stale, and the mind goes blank for lack of stimulation. Aristotle said that eggs originated in the womb and Aristotle could not be wrong. When nature was found to be different, it was nature that was at fault. It is no wonder that the men who began to look about them with seeing eyes, after the dark and middle ages came to a close, had great difficulty in divesting their minds of the curious and fantastic ideas that had accumulated during the two milleniums.

Throughout medieval times people believed that worms, flies and other crawling things were the spawn of humid, putrid substances; serpents came from women's hair that had fallen into water; mice could be produced by fermenting wheat with water for twenty-one days—and this was about the time of the Pilgrim Fathers.

By the beginning of the seventeenth century men were willing to observe directly and describe things for themselves, and while the obvious was hard to see, as always, the age of enlightenment began to dawn. And it seems to me to be a fitting start that the new knowledge that we now are building on begins with the chicken and the egg. The question was not whether the chick came from the egg, but where did the egg come from? If you clean a hen for the spit and look at what you are doing, it is obvious enough that a hen's eggs are formed in the ovary. The point is that for two thousand years those who cleaned hens did not care, and those who were interested in where eggs came from

10

only read books, and ancient ones at that. Not until 1604 did a gentleman with the imposing name of Hieronymus Fabricius ab Aquapendente make the connection and describe where hens' eggs came from—although the new and the old are still mixed up, for he also said that "the foetus of animals is engendered in one case from an ovum, in another from the seminal fluid, in a third from putrefaction: whence some creatures are oviparous, others viviparous, and yet others, born of putrefaction, or by spontaneous act of nature, automatically."

It was an age of beginnings, of inquiries into the nature of the human body and into nature at large. The search for origins went on apace, and in the last quarter of the seventeenth century we find a great surge of interest and excitement as the trail to the mammalian egg is followed to its end. De Graaf described the mammalian ovary and compared it with the birds', finding ovarian follicles half an inch across, though he missed the minute ovum within the follicle, and thought the embryo grew from the mysterious influence of the male semen upon the follicles of the ovary. He was getting close, but there was as yet no microscope to make the invisible world visible, no means of seeing sperm within the semen nor an egg the size of a pin point.

Follicles led to the encasement theory and to one of the most fascinating arguments I have ever encountered. It ran this way: all ova which were to create unborn generations were carefully enclosed one within the other, like a Chinese puzzle box, in the ovary of Eve. Each female generation since Eve has had one egg less, and the prophecy was rashly made that after two hundred million generations all human life would come to an end—the eggs would run out. The Church entered the fray triumphantly, for everything therefore went back to the primal creative act, and the loins of Adam and Eve, and gave biological proof of the inheritance of original sin.

No sooner had the Graafian follicle and the Church joined forces and the ovum been established as the one and only source of the embryo, than another Dutchman, van Leeuwenhoek, upset everything. He made microscopes, the first microscopes, 247 of them during the course of his life, and for the first time saw what lay below the limits of normal visibility. Among the many things he examined was semen, and he saw the infinite multitude of spermatozoa—animalcules, he called them—and concluded that these were the sole source of the embryo, upholding the old Egyptian-Greek idea that the mother was merely the field in which the seed grew, a concept that was embodied in English inheritance laws as late as the sixteenth century. And from here on, for nearly two hundred years, there was an open and acrimonious war between two opposing intellectual groups.

The microscope brought new sight, but you could hardly call it insight. For the new enthusiasts now saw the human face in the head of the sperm, compressed limbs and body in the tail—the sperm in fact contained the whole structure of a human being in miniature. And not only that, for the encasement theory was too good to lose: each little homunculus contained a smaller one, and so on ad infinitum —and the trail was traced to Adam, who after all took precedence over Eve.

The hottest arguments, in science at least, arise when two sides each have a hold of part of the truth and mistake it for the whole. The egg enthusiasts considered spermatozoa to be nothing but parasitic worms, and any resemblance a child might have to its father was thought to be the result of prenatal influence. Sperm protagonists were equally confident that the egg was just a shelter in which the little sperm could pass its critical phase of growth; and any resemblance the child might have to its mother was simply the result of maternal nourishment. Pieces of a story rarely make much of a tale, and now in our present enlightenment we know that the egg and sperm unite and together produce the embryo. The contest was a draw, and merely shows how argument and ignorance go hand in hand.

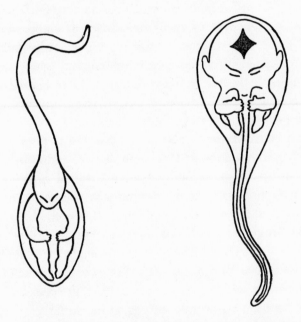

Eighteenth Century interpretations of human structure in spermatozoa: human beings in microscopic miniature.

13

2. to be and what to be

If a man should ever make a visit to Mars and return to report on the kinds of curious creatures he may find there, he will have difficulty in communicating his impressions in words alone unless what he describes is already partly familiar to us. Looking down a microscope at what is otherwise invisible is not so very different—in either case you enter a new world. In either case it is an adventure that must be experienced to be fully shared.

Much of my time as a biologist has been spent looking through a microscope at the beginnings of individual lives, partly in an effort to understand a little of how animals develop from eggs, partly and perhaps primarily in sheer fascination at the unfolding picture. It is something to be seen, although seen as action, and more and more you realize the truth of the philosopher Whitehead's statement that the process itself is the actuality. When you sit down in the early morning and watch a myriad dancing specks of spermatozoans buzzing around an egg, itself no larger than the smallest speck of dust to the naked eye, you are held entranced. When you see that egg divide into two, into four, eight, sixteen and more cells all closely united, and watch the ball of living substance gradually change its form until by evening, still small, it has a body and a tail, a simple eye

14

and an organ for balance—a miniature tadpole—you believe it has happened only because you have seen it. You can look at the events scientifically and do things to the egg or the embryo or the water in which it develops, and see what effect your interference has upon the outcome, as though you were warming up a clock or taking out this part or that to see what difference it might make to the way it runs; but in the end what holds your mind and eye is the way the clock keeps time and the steady transformation of an egg into a tadpole, or whatever else it might be, between dawn and dusk. The development of a living active organism from a seemingly inert egg, while you wait, is a miracle that never palls. So is the explosive vigor with which the process starts, when a sperm first enters an egg and releases the trigger.

The egg is launched on its course the instant the sperm hits its surface. Up to that moment its life has been sluggish, in a metabolic way, and the touch of the sperm is electrifying, like the kiss that wakened the sleeping beauty. And this is no idle metaphor for in every true sense of the word the egg is revitalized, and develops in consequence. Whether the egg is minute, though quick to develop, like the eggs of the sea squirts that I study, or enormous shell-protected gobs like the eggs of ostriches, or as small as ever and inaccessible, like those of elephants and human beings, the process is the same. An infinitely small spermatozoan, so small that ten thousand or more can be placed side by side and not cover an inch, must reach the surface of the egg; and it must reach the egg while there is still some of its limited energy left in the little lashing tail.

Such are the sex cells. Any small egg is much like another, no matter what kind of animal it finally becomes—a starfish egg and a human egg are about the same size and look much alike, semitransparent and about a two hundredth of an inch across, small enough by any measure except that of a spermatozoan. This is our starting point. All the nature of sex and the meaning of sex stems from it. By fair means or foul, sex cells must be brought together so that eggs may be fertilized; and eggs and sperm, for the most part, must come from different parents. And not all of it is simply for the sake of reproduction.

Many animals, as well as plants, can reproduce without involving sex cells or sexes or anything to do with sex. Reproduction itself is far more fundamentally a function of life and may or may not be bound up with eggs and sperm. Sea squirts are a case in point, and I bring them in because so much of my own studies have concerned them. They are common enough on the floor of shallow seas and along the shores throughout the world although they rarely attract attention. This is natural enough since they cannot move, are fixed vegetatively like plants to rocks and weeds and look like nothing else on earth. Many look like potatoes with two holes on the upper end, one for the intake and one for the output of water. Why put so much time on them? There are a number of reasons.

Some of these are personal, though not private. The development of any kind of egg, from the time of fertilization to the formation of an active organism, if sufficiently studied, throws light on the way all eggs develop. If I knew all about a sea squirt I could tell you a lot about a man. For a sea squirt egg becomes a little tadpole before it settles down and loses its tail and vegetates upon a certain spot—it has an interest all its own quite apart from a clear connection with the lordly race of backboned animals to which we our-

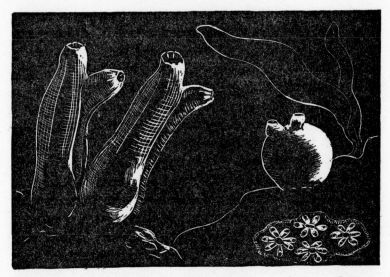

Seasquirts, or tunicates, growing attached to rocks on seafloor.

selves belong. To find them you must climb among the rocks and pools or mangrove bays at the edge of the sea, which is a harmless and most enjoyable occupation, though one that is all the better for a good excuse. Yet this is by the way—what has held my attention most and is the point of interest here is that sea squirts can reproduce by two entirely different means. They produce eggs and sperm in the usual way, and they produce small fragments of tissue, without any connection with sex cells, that develop just as readily into new sea squirts. Fertilized eggs and small buds of body tissue develop into new sea squirts indistinguishable from one another.

Nonsexual reproduction of this sort is fairly common among the lowlier forms of life. Many marine worms which produce ripe eggs and sperm at a certain time of the year at other times simply break up into numerous small frag-

17

ments, each of which transforms into a new worm. Even worms that do not do this naturally can be cut up into minute pieces and after a week or two you will find each piece has a new head and tail, and where there was one worm originally there now are many.

Jellyfish produce eggs or sperm as abundantly as any other animal, and shed them freely into the surrounding sea to get together and develop as best they can—a wasteful process at the best. Yet many of them at other times reproduce their kind by other means than eggs. For several years I have gone down to the coast in early spring, before the winter chill has left the sea, and trailed silk nets behind a boat to see what I could find. And on each occasion the net has caught hundreds of small but exquisitely beautiful jellyfish each in the process of growing miniature replicas of themselves, like shoots upon a tree. In some the budded offspring grow from the central pendulant mouth, in others in alternating sequence from around the rim. And as long as the water stays cold the process is repeated indefinitely —all reproduction is by bud formation and no sex cells are ever found. Vast populations of these transparent creatures build up in the sea by such means as this. Only when the sea gets warmer does budding cease and reproduction changes to eggs and sperm. The shift is dramatic. One day the net brings in only bud-producing jellyfish; two or three days later you find them with ovaries or testes but no buds; a little later when the eggs and sperm have all been shed I have towed the nets without avail—the cycle is finished, the sex cells are shed, their parents dead, and only the fertilized eggs remain drifting in the sea to represent the race. Yet eggs and sperm have been produced by every budded jellyfish, and each reproductive process, by buds or eggs, has its own distinctive value.

Jellyfish producing more jellyfish by budding them off from the rim and the mouth tube respectively.

This is the heart of it. A jellyfish that continually grows new jellyfish from points along its margin and a worm that breaks up into a hundred pieces, each of which grows into a new worm, reproduce their kind literally and completely. The chance that any of their offspring will be any different from themselves is very remote indeed—each is the spitting-image of the next—and while it all leads to large populations, the result is uniform and monotonous. If one dies then all die, should their watery world get a little too warm or muddy. It is the old story—there is danger in putting all of your eggs in one basket, although in this case it is not eggs that we are speaking of. In fact every egg is a basket by itself, for every egg is just a little different from any other.

19

And as eggs differ in little ways among themselves, so do spermatozoa.

Creatures that are born as buds are all alike, as identical as identical twins. Those that come from eggs, even from eggs which develop automatically without union with a sperm, are all a little different; although the differences are greatest when the eggs have been fertilized by spermatozoa, particularly when eggs and sperm have come from different parents. As a means of reproduction eggs are no better than buds. Both eggs and buds are units of reproduction, both illustrate the fact that a fragment of living tissue has the latent power to reproduce the whole, but only the eggs are concerned with the production of variety. The special nature of eggs and sperm is related to evolution, to adaptation to a changing environment, to colonizing distant regions that are different from the home territory, to producing novelties which may or may not be better than their parents. All the diversity of the human race, those long and short, wide and thin figures you see walking down the street; the redheads, blonds and brunettes, blue-eyed or brown, short-tempered or serene, all that makes people different, arises from the fact that eggs or sperm are manufactured all a little different from one another.

The unlikeness is all-pervading and each man stands alone. Only, lest we make too much of it, so does every toad. We not only look different, we differ in our chemistry. Otherwise it would be a simple matter to graft skin from one person to another to cover wounds or burns. It can be done of course, but at the best it is a temporary expedient, and even grafts of skin made from mother to child or from brother to brother survive transplantation for no more than a matter of weeks. After extensive surface injuries the

20

victim usually must supply his own tissue for grafting, from some other part of his body—a tiresome and contortionist exercise as a rule. And what is true for us is true for all; not even a mouse will fully accept a skin graft from any other mouse. Even blood transfuses safely only within certain limitations. If you receive blood from a person belonging to the wrong blood group it may kill you.

There are exceptions. Identical twins, which develop from one and the same egg, behave toward skin grafts as though they were a single individual, which in a sense of course is what they were to start with. They accept each other's skin as though it were their own. But prolonged and close inbreeding can produce practically the same result, at least in the case of mice. If mice are bred by brother-to-sister matings for more than twenty successive generations, they come to resemble one another almost as closely as if they were identical twins, and always accept each other's tissues. The differences that normally arise from the fact that eggs and sperm usually come from unrelated parents are here progressively neutralized. The outbreeding process is put into reverse, the basic purpose of sexual as distinct from any other kind of reproduction is counteracted—and the general result in the end is not so different from reproduction by buds, an uninteresting and hazardous uniformity.

So it really comes to this, that sexual reproduction is a device of nature to kill two birds with one stone. It takes care of reproduction as such, and it ensures that the offspring of any pair of parents will vary considerably among themselves. One generation produces the next and something new turns up every time. Such is the double role that the sex cells have to play, and all the rest of sex is built around it.

3. the virgin egg

If nature as a whole can be said to have an obsession it lies in the need to produce fertilized eggs and to launch them upon their career. And it calls attention to the difference between the sex cells—why should they be so different? The perennial human question concerning the equality of the sexes goes far beyond sex as we know it and finds its roots in the sex cells as such. Why are eggs and sperm so unlike, and what are their respective contributions to the organisms-to-be?

Much of it is simply a division of labor. It is difficult to be a jack-of-all-trades and do any particular job well. And the cell that is to develop into a new plant or animal must unite with another cell, and between them they must possess enough material to make something much more complex than they are to begin with. So one kind stores the substance and the other does the traveling. In this way they get together and have enough to build with.

Even the smallest egg is large for a cell, many times larger than a white corpuscle in your blood, while the egg of an ostrich may well be the largest cell in the universe. We will never know. But storing up material makes eggs round and large, and this alone puts any movement on their part to meet a sperm completely out of the question. So it is all left for the sperm to do. All the responsibility for reaching an egg is theirs and theirs alone. They are simply cells with a delicate tail for swimming and everything else reduced to a minimum.

Numbers are important too. At the best the chances are slight that any particular sperm will ever make contact with an egg, and astronomical numbers are always necessary for successful fertilization. The largest possible number, and therefore the smallest possible size, is the rule. In the case of eggs the problem is different—in fact it is a dilemma. For the larger the individual egg becomes, the farther it can progress along its course before it has to be an organism fending for itself. Large eggs are better than small eggs. Yet every animal and plant works on a budget and can set aside just so much material for producing sex cells. Large eggs means fewer eggs and that is not so good. The greater the number of eggs produced the more likely some of them will survive to carry on the race. And so every race and species is torn between producing large eggs and enough eggs. It is a difficult choice and there is no single answer— it all depends on circumstances, one creature does this and another does that, and one thing leads to another.

Cell for cell the sexes are not equal—a sperm is minute compared with even the smallest egg. Yet a male may hope to console himself with the thought that matter is not everything. What else is there? As a rule an egg must be fertilized by a sperm in order to develop, but it is only as a rule and far from being always. Masculine self-esteem gets shakier the more you look into the question.

It all started more than half a century ago when biologists were looking closely for the first time into the nature of the fertilization of an egg and of the processes involved—sheer

23

curiosity of the kind that killed the cat and led to the making of an atomic bomb. Only in this case it merely puts the male in his place.

The experiments made at that time have been repeated ever since. Every summer in marine laboratories on the coasts, students and others place ripe starfish eggs in sea water that has been tampered with, usually by the addition of a little organic acid, and they watch the eggs develop in consequence without the aid of spermatozoa at all. Apparently all the potentiality for development and the making of a new starfish is there in the egg by itself. All it needs is a little push to get it started.

Frog eggs are equally susceptible, although they need a somewhat different kind of push. It is a fascinating process and its practice is a common classroom exercise in most of the colleges throughout the land. It gives you an unwarranted god-like feeling. You need only some female frogs a month or two before the onset of their breeding season. If you inject one of them with extract of pituitary gland— that small but all-important gland that lies beneath the brain of every backboned animal from fish to man—the frog lays her eggs within twenty-four hours. It works almost every time and it is about the only way you can get fully ripened eggs entirely free from any sperm. For once they have been laid in a pond it is too late, and there would be spermatozoa around to confuse the issue.

The release of the eggs by pressing a physiological button is impressive enough, but making them develop by mechanical means is more than that. The jelly that surrounds each egg is carefully removed by rolling it gently on blotting paper, so that the naked egg is exposed. Then, with extreme care, you prick its surface with the point of a fine

24

glass needle. It is a delicate operation and the steadiest hand is all too clumsy, but out of a hundred so treated a score or two will start to divide and develop into tadpoles. And all such tadpoles will be males.

Only the human male seems inclined to play tricks with eggs like this—women are either busier or have more important things to do. Female frogs are made to lay eggs before their time, the eggs are made to develop without benefit of spermatozoa, but only males result. There is a suggestion of irony somewhere.

Actually there is a clue here to sex as distinct from sex cells. The fully ripened egg of almost any kind of animal, if it will develop at all without being fertilized by a sperm, develops into a male. It takes a double dose of something to become a female. In the case of frogs and human beings there are two kinds of sperm, although they all look alike. One kind carries that extra component that added to an egg makes a female, the other kind does not. Since the two kinds are produced in approximately equal numbers, the chances are the same that one or the other kind will fertilize an egg. The result is that males and females are normally produced in equal numbers. Pricked frog eggs lack the spermatozoan contribution and are doomed to develop into males, if they develop at all.

Parthenogenesis—the long name for a short process, and meaning origin from a virgin—has been brought about by methods such as these in a number of different animals, particularly among the so-called lower forms. Simply raising the temperature will often do it in the case of frog eggs. It has been only natural to wonder if it can be accomplished in a mammal.

In spite of ancient notions concerning conception and the

25

general belief that all conceptions in human beings were the result of a spirit of some kind entering the womb of the woman, there is no good evidence that in mammals, whether human or otherwise, eggs ever naturally develop without being fertilized by spermatozoa. Such an occurrence is not implausible for it does happen in bees and other creatures, but not in mammals. And I doubt whether it is ever a natural event in frogs or starfish.

Yet the thought lingers and sooner or later as you might expect, someone would attempt to make mammalian eggs develop without benefit of paternity. The victims have been rabbits. Ripe but unfertilized mammalian eggs, whether a rabbit's or some other's, are notoriously hard to obtain, and they are always few in number. Nearly thirty years ago in France the embryologist Champy discovered among a group of unfertilized rabbit eggs cultivated outside the body— although at the body temperature—that some eggs underwent divisions as though they had been fertilized. Gregory Pincus, in America, followed this up and tried out all the tricks we know that have made the eggs of lower animals develop spontaneously. But only an occasional egg ever reached a recognizable stage in embryo formation. The possibility of parthenogenesis seemed to be present, yet something was wrong.

Apparently it is one thing to cause a mammalian egg to divide, it is another entirely to keep it going in a normal manner; which is not surprising when you consider that the mammalian egg is adjusted to develop in the tubes and womb of the mother. So Pincus treated the unfertilized eggs as before and then transplanted them into virgin rabbits. Out of a large number of trials, some of these virgins bore normal rabbits. In many others the embryos were well advanced but died prematurely. It is not very promising, though perhaps one day we may breed our cows without utilizing bulls. Perhaps it would be better if we cannot, for the human race so far shows no sign of knowing when or where to stop.

The immediate interest of these rabbit experiments, to me at least, is that all the born and unborn offspring that have come from these unfertilized eggs have been females.

The explanation goes back to the ripening of the egg. Starfish eggs, frog eggs, rabbit and human eggs all ripen normally in essentially the same way. When the fully grown egg leaves the ovary, whether to be shed into the sea if it is a starfish or to enter and lie in the oviduct if it is a mammal, it has to go through a process of division before it is ready to be fertilized. It divides not into two equal parts as a cell usually does, but into a minute polar cell and one so large it looks like the original egg. And the event is important out of all proportion to its magnitude.

This particular division of the egg cell is possibly the most important in all of nature and throughout earthly time. For it is during this division that the differences arise that make one egg different from the next, that supply the raw material for evolution and adaptation to a changing world. This is the general importance of it. The egg is different because of this division, and the polar cell is simply a by-product of the process. Yet sometimes the polar division is suppressed and the egg may still develop. This, according to another French investigator, is exactly what happens in those eggs that produce parthenogenetic female rabbits. The eggs retain a double quantity of the female component and develop into females. The rabbit eggs that do not retain the substance of the polar cell but ripen fully, do not

27

develop at all unless they are fertilized by a sperm. I doubt if this indicates the final fate of the human male, but it does suggest that if we ever succeed in producing a race with eggs that develop spontaneously the result will be a purely female population capable of carrying on more or less indefinitely without the male—in fact no males could be expected, unless the system became elaborated.

This may seem to be a fantastic speculation. I think in all probability that is true. But if it appears to be a most unlikely prospect, at least it is one of the might-have-beens. It has happened to other creatures, and it goes on in almost any pond or pool in spring or summer. In any of these you can find the water fleas: Daphnia in particular. They swim

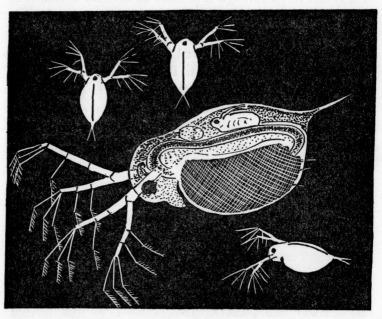

Daphnia, the water flea, with parthenogenetic young inside brood pouch.

with a jerky movement—hence their name—but they are as crustacean as a crayfish and are not insects at all. Like all living things they belong to their environment, and what they have to do, in an almost literal sense, is to make hay while the sun shines. For they are specialists in living in small pools and even barnyard puddles, feeding on everything that is microscopic, whether it be plant cells, debris or bacteria. As long as there is food of this sort and a certain amount of water, Daphnia and its kind can flourish. Sometimes when you come across a pond or a meadow pool the water is cloudy with them, the swarms are so dense. If you look closely you can see each small individual beating its way through the water with a pair of oarlike appendages, directing its movement with a solitary eye.

These are creatures of a transient and intermittent world —they flourish when the water comes, like flowers in springtime, and when the water has gone there is no more to be seen than the seeds of an annual plant.

The eggs hatch out as miniatures of the parent: a statement that means more than it usually does, for not only does a young Daphnia look very much like another one, it is a female like its mother. In spring after rains or melting snow returns water to the pools every member of the brood which hatches out is a female. There are no exceptions.

As the water warms and food becomes more plentiful the first brood of females matures and they in turn produce successive broods, each brood being carried in a sheltered pouch on the upper side of the parent. And each such brood in turn is entirely female. No males are present and none is required—the eggs develop without them and parthenogenesis is the rule. How it is that the eggs of Daphnia are able to develop spontaneously in the absence of sper-

29

matozoa I believe is beyond our present understanding, although it concerns the metabolic peculiarities of the eggs growing in the ovary. The reason that the Daphnia broods are all female is the same as for the rabbits of virgin birth —the polar cell of the ripening egg is retained, the double dose of the sex determinant is present, and the outcome is female.

Yet this is far from being the whole story, and when you put it all together it seems that Daphnia is exquisitely adapted to the little world in which it lives. Given the ideal conditions the Daphnia community remains exclusively female; but this is an everchanging universe, whatever its scale may be, and Daphnia no more than we can keep things perfect. The better the conditions the faster they breed, and the more they breed the more crowded the community becomes and the less food there is to go around—the time of trouble arrives. The response is almost miraculous.

The signal may be the lack of space that comes from over-crowding, perhaps the irritation that even the lowliest forms of life exhibit when the course of travel is continually being interrupted; it may be the sudden shortage of food that follows a population peak, or a sudden drop in temperature. A cold night and a chilly day may indicate the end of summer; overcrowding may forecast either lack of food or lack of water to live in. Whatever it is, and all may be effective, the response is the same and it is a striking one. There are two steps in it.

The first change is that broods of males appear in addition to the females. The males when grown are smaller, redder and more active, for their role is to catch on to and mate with a female. Their redder blood may or may not be significant. What brings them into being is another matter.

30

All that is necessary is that the eggs complete their ripening before development starts. The polar cell is given off, only a single unit of the sex determinant remains within the egg —and a male develops instead of a female. The environmental change affects the maternal organism so that the polar division of the grown egg is no longer suppressed, and the rest follows. It leaves us with the original problem— how do the eggs manage to develop without the stimulus of a sperm?

Only some females in the community react like this and produce male offspring. Others go right ahead producing female broods, which shows that even in a purely amazonian community of parthenogenetic females, individuals react differently to a given set of circumstances. They are not all alike no matter what they seem to be.

A scattering of males through the virgin paradise is the first step only. If the signal was a false alarm no harm is done, the females go on producing female broods and the males simply live out their lives without any propagative purpose—as thwarted as in the Greek play *Lysistrata*, where all the women went on connubial strike for the political welfare of the state.

Yet in Daphnia society if conditions go from bad to worse the second step is called into play. A cell in each female ovary grows to form an egg larger than any produced before —and it completes its final process of polar division. If it could develop spontaneously it would be a male. But this time it does not and fertilization by one of the males already present is essential. These are the winter eggs that become enclosed in cases so tough they are impermeable to water and are able to survive from one season to the next, like the well-protected seeds of plants. Females emerge—never a male—because the sperm contributed the additional unit of sex determinant that usually came from the polar cell. And they emerge only in the spring or after such time that the shells have been cracked by alternate freezings and thawings or drying out—only when water gets in do they complete their development and start the cycle over again.

Daphnias are aquatic creatures and this is sex and reproduction exploited to take advantage of the peculiar little universe of their choice—all for the sake of racial survival under difficult conditions. Only in the insect world do we see how the system is worked to create a society.

4. hermes and aphrodite

We tend to take the sexes for granted. Robins and human beings are unmistakably male or female and it seems to be the only natural state. Yet this is far from being the case, and it would be intriguing to speculate on how different human affairs might have been had we taken one of the possible alternative paths in the course of our evolution in the dim and distant past.

The study of the sex cells alone takes us about as far back in time as it is possible to go. Even the eggs of a bath sponge, which is animal and not a plant, have much in common with the eggs of humans. They are of about the same size and appearance, they mature in the same particular way, and you get the impression that eggs of a certain general kind came into being very early in the history of life. Spermatozoa seem to clinch the point. The sperm of sponge and jellyfish, worm and snail, fish, bird and man look alike, have virtually the same structure and activity, the same limited life and the same role to play. I doubt if there is anyone who can look at spermatozoa under a microscope and tell for sure what animal they came from. There are differences to be sure, but they are mostly small compared with what there is in common. The sex cells as we know them appear

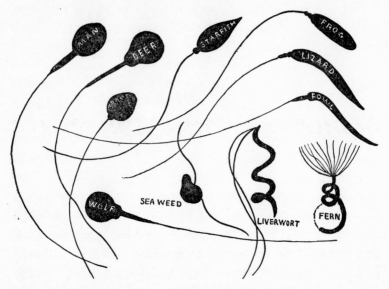

Spermatozoa of various animals and plants.

to be common property of the animal kingdom as a whole. They must have come into being at the beginning of things, more than a billion years ago.

All of the present takes root in the past and what is most fundamental goes the furthest back. You have to go to seaweeds and other aquatic plants to find sex cells that are markedly different from those of animals, and even then the similarities are striking. The male cells of plants have a double propulsive tail-like whip in place of the single one of a spermatozoan. It means I think that the differences, or division of labor, between sex cells, that unite together in fertilization, have been independently acquired in the plant and animal kingdoms; but that the coming together in pairs is itself so basic to life that it precedes the separation of the kingdoms.

What is true of the sex cells is almost as true of the sexes, although in a different way. Male and female individuals that produce sperm and eggs respectively are specialists just as definitely as the sex cells themselves. Those sea squirts that I have spent so much time with are a case in point. They have no sexes. Each individual of every kind is both male and female, true hermaphrodites, in fact. In the great majority of them the ovary and testes mature simultaneously and oviduct and sperm duct are distended with ripe eggs and sperm. At the most you can say that the eggs are more readily fertilized by sperm reaching them from another individual than by sperm of their own parentage. I have worked with them a lot, collecting the animals from their attachments at low tide and stripping them of their sex cells in the laboratory later on, in the same way that hatchery men strip fish of their eggs and milt, only here you can get both from one and the same individual. For the most part my purpose has been the study of developmental processes for their own intrinsic interest. But there is always the thought and my belief that this group of inert marine animals represents the ancient stock from which all back-boned animals once arose—that for all their present special peculiarities I am looking at relics of the beginning of my own racial history, and that in the beginning we were all hermaphrodites.

This seems to be the starting point for almost every large group of animals—for molluscs and crustaceans as well as vertebrates, not to mention some of the lesser folk. And in every case the separate sexes have been evolved out of the original hermaphrodite individuals. Each division of the animal kingdom has separated the sexes into two kinds of individuals, independently within its own family tree. It is plausible, and separation is simply the division of labor once again—males and females can do more apart than they can when combined as one. Among the gods of ancient Greece the fleet Hermes and seductive Aphrodite signified more than any hermaphroditic union.

We seem to be fairly content with our lot, but I think we would have been equally content, or unquestioning at least, with whatever sexual pattern we might have found ourselves a part of. Those creatures that are well-balanced, co-equal hermaphrodites cannot complain, being what they are, but I imagine they would have accepted their earthly status even if they had minds capable of such self-knowledge. As it is they—the earthworms, the slugs and the snails of the woods and fields, hedgerows and gardens—go about their silent vital business in the damp darkness of spring and summer nights.

These are animals of the land—not like sea squirts and others that can scatter their eggs and sperm freely into surrounding water without precaution for their survival— and the eggs must be fertilized before they are laid. Full and mutual mating takes place, and sperm passes from each member of a pair into the body of the other, ready to meet the eggs before they are laid.

The night or some dark secluded place is needed by snails for the safety it provides. Earthworms require the night for more than that, for they need the humid air of night to keep from drying out when they emerge above the ground, while the light of the sun would kill them quite apart from its heat. And so on the lawn during the darkness of warm moist nights you may find them lying side by side in pairs, exchanging sperm so that the benefits of outbreeding will be conferred upon their offspring—so that the brood will

36

Garden snails, hermaphrodites, in process of mating.

have greater variety and some will be better suited than others to the particular soil they find to live their lives in.

Garden slugs go about their duties even more circumspectly, perhaps because they present a more delectable meal to any wandering shrew hunting for its supper. They leave the stones and crevices and heavy foliage of their earthy level and crawl up tree trunks and out onto branches. There a pair that may have made the journey together suspend themselves jointly by a cord of mucus, to hang in safety in the air while their mutual exchange proceeds. Then each returns and goes its separate way to lay fertilized

37

eggs in its own good time. The hermaphroditic system works well for those that have it—but, and this seems to be significant, all of these are sluggish or immobile creatures, with no pun intended. I cannot recall a speedy hermaphrodite that functions as both sexes simultaneously. Why this should be I think is anyone's guess.

When we turn to the sea and to its crustaceans we find

Land slugs mating at night, hanging in safety by mucous cord from branch of tree.

a comparable situation. Crabs and lobsters are as separately sexed as you or I but some of their relatives are not. Those little white barnacles that cover the rocks between the tides and make walking barefoot comparable to fire walking are as crustacean as they can be, in spite of being unable to move about. And once again it is these permanently anchored animals that are the hermaphrodites of their class. Each produces eggs and sperm in season, each broods its offspring within the shelter of the shell—but only those can mate that are within reach of one another. An isolated barnacle is fated to be both an old maid and a bachelor.

The choice between being a hermaphrodite and in having separate sexes is not always a sharp one. Barnacles do not travel at all except when newly hatched; as sexually mature adults they are rooted to a spot. Separation of the sexes would place them in a worse predicament than before. But certain shrimps, one of them a common one on the Atlantic coast, are hermaphrodites that act as though they are not. For a long time they were thought to be simply male and female.

Each young shrimp grows up to be a male and is fully and functionally a male when about half the size of the females. If he grew no more he would probably remain in that condition. But growth goes on, and as the next season approaches he finds his masculinity has become a thing of the past—the testes within his body shrink and produce no more spermatozoa; but ovaries grow alongside. And as full growth is reached, the shrimp that had been a male becomes a typical female, ready to lay her eggs. If an individual that is both male and female in the course of its life is a hermaphrodite, then the shrimp qualifies for the name. But the sexes have become separate nevertheless, though the

39

separation is in time and not between different individuals. As far as I can see it is a system that works as well as any other means of separation. When your mind transposes it to humanity there is no end to the fantasies you can dream. Men would be half the size and half the age of women, with the prospect of maternity always ahead of them. What presumptuous male dictator would ever have a chance to throw his weight around? And how much greater would be the reminiscent wisdom of old age. It impinges at every point.

The association of the hermaphroditic condition with a more or less sluggish or rooted existence is a correlation, not an explanation. It happens that in every major division of the animal kingdom the faster and more adventurous kinds have separate sexes, the stay-at-homes combine them. The oyster on its rock changes sex from male to female and back again once or twice a year—it is hermaphrodite in time if not at once—but the equally molluskan but intelligent octopus and the squids, large and small, that drive themselves by jet propulsion through the ocean, have sexes as sharply separated and highly evolved as any other living creature. Why?

I do not think that speed or action has much to do with it directly—the presence of one or both of the reproductive glands has little to do with locomotion. Yet the correlation exists and perhaps the connection reads better the other way. Is speed, or what speed involves in the nature of animal structure and sensory equipment, an outcome of the sexes? I am thinking aloud, but this may be the way of it.

It goes something like this. We have already seen that sexual reproduction is only one method of reproduction, and that reproduction as such does not necessarily involve

40

two parents. Under ideal circumstances a single cell could reproduce the whole organism. The union of two cells, as in the fertilization of an egg, concerns the evolutionary side of things—and makes the offspring different from its parents. Without this there could be no change from one generation to the next. Inbreeding—brother-to-sister matings—reduce such differences almost to a minimum. Self-fertilization by a hermaphrodite goes even further, and tends to neutralize completely the advantages of the sexual aspect of reproduction. Therefore the problem that has always faced the hermaphrodites is how to avoid fertilizing their own eggs with their own sperm. In the case of slugs and barnacles organs have been developed that make it almost physically impossible. Shrimps and oysters work according to a timetable that puts the two sexes out of phase. Sea squirts have a smaller margin of safety and are not always successful. In all of these the mechanism for avoiding self-fertilization is somewhat makeshift; and at the best the rate at which hermaphrodite animals can evolve during the course of generations is likely to be slow. Any group that managed to separate the sexes made cross-fertilization the permanent state of affairs; self-fertilizations became forever impossible, and the rate of evolution could be speeded up. And I think this in all likelihood was a necessity or a condition for the changes that transformed primitive slow-moving animals into the lithe, active and adaptive creatures they have now become. There must have been a driving need in all competing groups of animals for each group to have independently found ways and means to evolve two separate sexes out of the combination. Yet they have done it and each group has found a way of doing it that is in some degree distinctively its own; but that is another story.

41

5. on getting together

Once you have made a decision you have to live with it. When sexes became separate from one another and their possessors began to go places independently, they were faced with the problem of being in the right place at the right time. If it wasn't a new problem it was an old one greatly intensified. And it has been a problem ever since— dating and mating is a headache for most of nature and not just a case of how boy meets girl.

Moonlight is seductive and a night in June is fraught with meaning. Couples are drawn together to look at the stars and the following June there is a wedding. Yet the moon and stars at any other time may be effective, and other creatures feel its influence besides ourselves. Apart from human emotions and sentiments, the basic requirement for all living things that are of one sex only and that move freely about is to pair off for the purpose of breeding at such a time when both are in full reproductive capacity, and in a place that is safe enough. Safety may be for mating only, or it may be needed for the eggs as well, if they are to be laid at once. But both time and place must be arranged and a sign is always valuable.

The moon waxes and wanes. The moon-struck tides rise to a biweekly peak and down again, and the double clock keeps time for a host of oceanic creatures. The grunion is one of them—a smelt about six inches long that is a southern Californian delicacy. At times it is so abundant that its spawning periods are festive occasions for thousands of Californians, cars being parked bumper to bumper for many miles along the coastal roads, with beach fires and the moon lighting the scene. Hats, bare hands, almost anything is used to catch them, and roasted over the fires they make excellent fare. On the second, third and fourth nights after the moon is full, throughout spring and summer when the tide is high, the fish swim up the beach with the breaking waves to the highest point they can reach. The female digs into the sand tail-foremost and deposits her eggs three inches below the surface, and during the process the male arches around her and fertilizes them as they are shed. Then, with their racial duties accomplished, they slip back into the sea in the wash of a succeeding wave. Ten to twelve days later, when high tides begin to arrive again, the youngsters hatch out and swim down to the sea in their turn.

It looks like a fairly simple appointment—riding the high tides after the moon is full; but nature is rarely as simple as she looks. Local residents along the beaches know that the grunion run at the dark of the moon as well as when the moon is full. It is always well after sunset, sometimes as late as midnight, and it doesn't seem to matter much whether the moon is shining or not.

So suspicion shifts from the moon to the tides which the moon controls. The high spring tides come every two weeks, not just once a month, and this it seems is the rhythm to which the grunion and their developing eggs are attuned. It is a rhythm that pervades the fish as a whole, the periodic growth of ovaries and testes as well as a short migratory response to tides and nighttime. But the lunar rhythm is there, even though indirectly—it is not just a coincidence like the monthly period of a woman.

Yet grunion swim in schools, males and females are always together, and their problem is to lay their eggs in the right place and to fertilize them at the time of laying. The males have no trouble in finding and following females. In the depths of the ocean it is another matter.

The deep sea is both dark and cold; animals are small and few and far between; plants there are none; and there is water, miles of it, up and down as well as round about. How to find a mate and carry on the race is an almost hopeless problem that has led to some drastic solutions. Certain little fishing frogs, fish related to the large and ugly northern angler, have found one as peculiar as any.

In such a world as this sight is unimportant and much depends upon chance encounter. Fishing frogs cannot wait until both males and females are fully grown before the search for a partner begins. And it is the same old pattern —the males hunt the females, only they start searching almost as soon as they are able to swim. Hunting in the dark like this, where space is so extensive, takes all of the males all of their time to have any chance of meeting a female. And as soon as a young male gets close enough to recognize the opposite sex, he takes a grip on the female with his jaws wherever he can get a hold. It is the last bite he ever takes, for male lips and female flesh fuse together and the small male remains for the rest of his life a dwarf parasite attached to the body of his spouse. He may have attached to her side or to the middle of her forehead, and he may not be the only male to do so. Thereafter he will

44

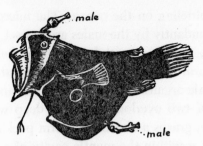

*Deepsea frogfish with dwarf male
attached to her forehead and to her
body.*

always be at the right place at the right time, ready to shed
sperm into the water whenever the female sheds her eggs.
The eggs will be cross-fertilized and the race will go on in
an adaptable form. But the individuality of the male is
sacrificed in the process. His mouth, jaws, teeth, fins, and
gills all degenerate; he is fed from the blood stream of the
female, for their blood vessels unite; and even the shedding
of his sperm is controlled by the chemistry of her blood.

And this far from land we should take a look at one or
two other inhabitants of the open sea—we can dry out later
on.

Squid and octopuses have developed sight and touch,
intelligence and swimming powers as good as those of any
fish, although they are as molluscan as the slug and oyster
and no relation to the vertebrates. They have separate
sexes, take a lot of trouble with their eggs, and in their own
way are a match for the grunion and the fishing frog.

A squid is built for speed and swims in schools like fish
—as oceanic as anything alive. Some have bodies twenty
feet long, with a head bearing ten tentacles each thirty feet
long, and a pair of eyes a foot or so across. Mating is accomplished while at sea, a scene that must be a little like

battleships refueling on the ocean. The microscopic sperm produced abundantly by the males are not set free in clouds in the water, for eggs must be fertilized before they are laid. The sperm are wrapped up into cigar-shaped packets within the male organs. When mating time arrives the male thrusts one of two overlong tentacles deep within its own mantle cavity, grasps a cluster of sperm packets, withdraws it and thrusts it within the mantle cavity of a female swimming alongside. Then the two go their own ways and the female utilizes the sperm at a later place and time more suitable for the laying of her eggs.

This is the basic reproductive pattern of these animals. It is carried to its extreme by the Argonauts, or Paper Nautilus, an octopus with two names that mean a sailor. These are mollusks of the sea floor that lack the streamlining of the squid and have eight arms or tentacles instead of ten. But otherwise they are much the same.

The female is just an ordinary sort of octopus distinguished chiefly by the way she cradles her eggs: she makes a lovely paper-white shell between one large tentacle and her round body and lays and keeps her eggs within it. But this is after the event of mating.

The male is small—a dwarf in fact—though never a parasite like its fishing-frog counterpart. It is not more than an inch long, to the female's six, and it mates in the usual squid and octopus manner. One long arm thrusts a cluster of sperm packets deep within the mantle cavity of the female. Perhaps, being so small, it has been a risky business and in the past many got in so far they couldn't get out, a catastrophe for both the partners. However it was, the rule at present is for every little Argonaut male to snap off his dedicatory arm at its base, even before the insertion is com-

46

pleted, leaving the arm with its load of sperm within the female where they are sure to do their work. And before the next season comes the male has grown another arm and can repeat the process—he can, that is, if he lives that long. Small males are dispensable, usually short-lived, and are readily produced. The main burden of reproduction rests heavily upon the females.

The getting together of males and females is a problem

Argonaut or Paper Nautilus, with dwarf male in foreground showing long swollen arm containing sperm, and female in background forming a shell with her own large arm.

47

only when numbers are few and space is large. In most cases the traveling done by prospective parents is to get to a certain place because it is the best or the traditional place for laying eggs or rearing young. The spectacular migrations of birds and fish and even mammals for the most part have nurseries as their destination. The two sexes may have been close together all the time, or much of it at least; males and females journey together or else follow the same trail to a place that offers both food and safety to their prospective progeny. Salmon swim against the currents and upstream for many hundreds of miles simply to reach the streams where eggs can be fertilized and laid with a fair chance of survival. They return to an ancestral home, and sex and reproduction come into play only after their arrival. Eels migrate the other way, downstream to their destiny in deep water below the Sargasso Sea, to spawn and die. The mature females leave their ponds to enter the streams and rivers and finally the sea, then to travel a thousand miles through what seem to be uncharted watery wastes to find their destination. The males reach the same place at the same time, but they never left the sea in the first place and start their journey from the coasts and estuaries. How they find their way nobody knows, nor how they find their partners in the dark abyss. Perhaps they don't; perhaps a massive turbulent maelstrom of spawning eels sheds milt and eggs together in the still water and enough of the eggs get fertilized to launch a new generation toward the continental coasts.

The way of the pathfinder is mysterious, whether it be that of bird, beast or fish, but the purpose is generally unmistakable: to get where they should be when the time for breeding arrives and to propagate the race.

48

6. the choice of a mate

The law of supply and demand operates for the sexes. In a community where boys are more numerous than girls they tend to strive among themselves for dominance or attention. When boys are at a premium they sit back and take their pick. The balance is readily tipped. This is human behavior of a kind, but it is not by any means distinctive of our species. All the way down the line, from men to fish and beetles, there is a struggle for attention. It is a masculine occupation, for the simple reason that there is usually an excess of males no matter how well equated the sexes may be to start with. A male and female are never equal, they are different—and balancing one quality against another cannot equate a man and a woman any more than it can a painter and a poet.

The standard sex ratio of, on an average, one male for every female is not a mathematical balance that has been slowly gained in the course of distant ages, out of a wide range of alternative possibilities. It is I believe an imposition from the start, and living things, both plant and animal, have had to make the best of it. Even if it is the best, it has been a case of Hobson's choice.

It all goes back to the beginnings of life, to the union of

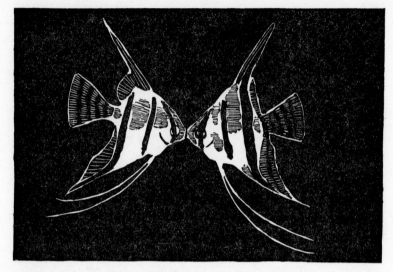

Angelfish male and female establish bond.

reproductive cells in pairs, and to the evolution of hermaphrodites with male and female glands combined in a single individual.

From there on the problem has been, figuratively speaking, to split that individual into two, each carrying a single sex. The basic mechanisms are fairly simple, in principle at least, if not in detail. Human beings and frogs and the great majority do it one way—by producing two kinds of spermatozoa and one kind of egg; the result is two kinds of offspring in approximately equal numbers, male and female respectively. Birds and many other forms manage the other way round—two kinds of eggs and only one kind of spermatozoa; the outcome is the same. The only alternative is two kinds of each, both of eggs and spermatozoa alike, and that leads to a mess, which a little arithmetic can show.

The one-to-one ratio may be the ideal—for every female

to have her own partner; the greatest variation is then produced among the succeeding generation. But unless conditions are changing fast, such extreme variability and racial adaptability may be more than is either necessary or desirable. In practice it rarely happens, and as a rule only a relatively small percentage of the males in an animal community are actual breeders. All of the mating is performed by only some of the males. This is not a universal state but it is a common one.

The males struggle for the privilege of mating, whatever the subsequent penalty they may have to pay. Just as the knights of old used to joust for the fair hand of a lady, even a crab struts all out of proportion to the importance of the affair. Most of us who have strolled along the Atlantic beaches—when not too crowded—have watched the fiddler crabs as they pop in and out of their burrows and scuttle sidewise on the sand when the tide is out.

The females have two small claws and seem to be as demure as their sex should be. The males have one small claw and one claw that is enormous, far too large for the little crab that owns it. They look like the guardians of the fiddler community, but like all crabs that I have seen they meet danger by scuttling for their lives. The large claw is for purely domestic purposes: for sparring with another male to determine who is who; though all the vanquished has to do, should he lose his weapon, is to grow a new one —a frequent event. But in the mating season a male fiddler will stand in view of a passing female and brandish his claw before her. If she keeps going he may dash ahead and wave it aloft again. No threat is involved—it is simply a wolf call, with dishonorable intentions. If the lady is in tune she recognizes the signal; but without his claw he hasn't a

51

Two male stagbeetles, with overdeveloped armor, fight over a female.

chance—he is without his badge of maleness. The claw has little other meaning, has seemingly no advantage to the species, and the females at least get along just as well without it. It is in part a threat to other males, partly a form of sex appeal and recognition.

The grotesque armor and great mandibles of the male stag beetles are in the same category—the result of a purely internal struggle for the possession or favor of the female. The males in this case fight it out and the larger and stronger individuals succeed in mating, while the others do not or at least not so often. Up to a point this is all to the good, it maintains a race of healthy males whose vigor is passed on to the next generation. But in both crab and beetle the process has gone far beyond the primary objective—overdevelopment of any particular structure or quality in animal or man can be as much a liability as an asset.

Like so many other people I have at one time kept guppies in a home aquarium, and even tried my hand at

52

keeping swordtails. Both fish bear their young alive and eggs must be fertilized within the female; mating involves actual contact so that sperm can be introduced.

I have always assumed that the guppy sexes recognize each other instinctively, for the vividly colored male is so different from the female. But it seems that even a guppy has to learn. If males are reared from birth in separate aquaria they will attempt to mate as readily with another male as with a female; and the first approach to mating is to bite the rear part of the other fish. If a male is so attacked, it turns upon the offender, and males soon learn to avoid other males in consequence—the bright male color pattern serves as a warning to keep away. The reaction is entirely visual and an experienced guppy displays his charms only to a female—not that it makes much difference, since he usually mates so suddenly and fast that there simply is not time enough for any preliminaries.

Swordtails are similar in their relationships, if not in looks. The male differs from the female not only in being smaller but in having a long golden sword extending from the lower margin of the tail fin; it functions as a sexual stimulant and may be rubbed along the side of a female. And inasmuch as this fish actually produces an excess of males—how it does so is another matter—there is inevitably competition among them, and the most stimulating males pass on their more seductive swords to the next generation. This accounts for the length of the sword but not for its brilliant colors. These apparently have the same meaning as they do in the guppy. While male swordtails fight each other in the presence of a female, they are unable to recognize one another if they are reared from birth in isolation and will attempt to mate with either sex. Yet they

53

learn quickly and do not forget, and experiments show that the colored sword is the cue.

Bird watchers have noted that the greater the display the less the fight. It holds for fish and for humans too—a bully calls for a coward every time. And for color-sensitive fish a threat of color can mean a lot. The vivid but ugly dragonets that live in shallow east-Atlantic waters show this clearly. When two males meet in full splendor there is rarely a fight—one lowers his colors and flees ingloriously. Young males or unready females both flee from such a sight, although a ripe female when so confronted is attracted and swims to the side of the male. Sex recognition is involved just as much as male antagonism—the female recognizes the male by his colors, the male knows a female because she doesn't run away. Male bluster does double duty.

There are dangers in this sort of thing. The overanxious male becomes imposed upon. Since mating and its implicit urge to reproduce is so important to him, nature has a way of putting him to work. Sea catfish lay the largest eggs of any bony fish, but they drop them in muddy coastal waters unfit for any eggs; the male gathers them in his capacious mouth, often several dozen of them, all marble size, and incubates them there for months on end, under duress not to feed until paternal chores are ended. A small Chilean frog manages a little better. The male gulps up the dozen or more eggs the female lays and keeps them in his vocal pouch, in the moist safety of his own saliva. He hides until they are ready to emerge as froglets, though he can eat when he gets a chance without danger of swallowing his offspring. He cannot croak, that goes without saying, but in any case the croaking days are more or less over by the time eggs are being laid.

54

Yet it takes a fish and a bird to cast the mantle of maternity entirely over the male—in both the sea horse and the phalarope the turnabout is complete. The pelvic fins of a mature male sea horse are modified to form a brood pouch, and a male invites a female to mate with him by approaching her with his pouch wide open. If repulsed he swims quickly to another and keeps it up until one of them responds to his provocative attitude by depositing eggs inside his pouch. There they are fertilized and the pouch closed up; and until they hatch and are ready to escape through a hole at the top the male has an unmistakably pregnant shape.

Seahorses: at left, female transfers eggs to brood pouch of male where they are fertilized; at right, brooding males, one liberating offspring.

55

The female phalarope is a striking little oceanic bird with none of the usual drabness of her sex. She lays her eggs and goes her way and it is the male that sits upon the nest and incubates them. That may be fair enough—it depends on your point of view—but the male in this case has the dull garment of the female. Male and female not only have exchanged their parental roles, apart from the unchanged nature of their sex cells, they have exchanged their dress. A man should be able to mind the baby without putting on a skirt.

PART TWO

THEIR WORLD, NOT OURS

7. the great emergence

It is time to step on to dry land and get closer to our own immediate world; but we have come so lately into the scene it takes time to find our place. The backboned animals of which we are one entered a world on land that was already well colonized and was open to exploitation. We have reaped where we did not sow—and we do it yet. The stage that we and our kind now occupy was made without our help, without any thought of us, and we need to give it scrutiny; it is a world that was not created for us or by us, although it is ours to enjoy. There is abundant life and color, with sex playing its full creative part: a role that to us is at times both comic and tragic.

Our planet has been changing since the very beginning. Life appeared upon its surface, was cradled by the ocean, and the water and salts now pervade all living substance, however remote in place and time it may be from the sea at present. The primeval world of life was entirely wet and salty—our blood still is—and this conditions everything we do and are, and all of nature too. And so life on land for every kind has been a double effort—to stay wet inside while living in a dry environment and to support oneself out of water against the pull of gravity. These are the passwords to existence for flower, beetle and human being alike. Sexual reproduction alone has made it possible, for only organisms capable of adaptive change have been able to make the transit.

This I believe is the key to understanding the world around us and ourselves within it. The past lives on into the present and sets the course for future growth. We are creatures born of water, made mostly of water, living on dry land with only the gaseous air surrounding us, looking across the universe to distant stars. I find it hard to comprehend, let alone convey, the magnitude of the event—the conquest of the land by watery creations that became transformed themselves during the process of their emergence. But without the adaptability and the continual production of living novelties in succeeding generations, stemming from only the sexual form of reproduction, none of this could have happened. It is evolution at its most dramatic, and sex is its parent.

The past is like a play in several acts, of which the first is marine and then fresh water, interminably protracted. The land is bare and barren. In the second the air is humid and becomes more so all the time. We are taken back to the age of fishes, the early Devonian period, some three hundred million years ago when the first tentative steps were taken by plants and animals from the edge of fresh waters to the margin of the land. It was an invasion so slow that it took time beyond our counting, and, if backboned animals are included, it embraced both the beginning and the end of the age of the coal forests. When it was over the Devonian and Carboniferous periods had come and gone, and the dry, scorching winds of the succeeding Permian took the place of the mists and made deserts where swamplands and tree-fern forests had been. The invasion came in three waves—plants, then those animals that are now the host of creeping, crawling and flying creatures of the world about us and, somewhat belatedly, the four-legged vertebrates from which we ourselves arose. At the moment I am concerned with the first two of these waves. Between them they established and developed the world that we now claim for our own; and they go their own way in spite of all that we try to do.

Each emergent group has had to succeed in two ways, before emancipation from water could be said to be complete. Plants; the many-legged, many-jointed creatures; and the vertebrates had first to survive out of water and had then to breed out of water. To live out of water is one thing, and it needs a book to tell the story; reproduction out of water is another, and this involves both sexual and nonsexual reproductive devices.

From the very beginning of things plants have gone one way and animals another, and yet it is remarkable to what an extent they have paralleled each other, particularly with regard to sex.

The background is marine, although now we can stay on shore and look at it. Most rocky shores have festoons of seaweed, but for years I never thought of the weeds as doing any more than growing. Yet the fronds of the common sea wrack ripen in season and liberate either eggs or sperm into the surrounding water. Eggs become fertilized and settle down, and some of those that fall on stony ground grow and reproduce in turn. Sex cells of male and female type are present among the lowest as well as the highest plants, although I believe that the plants have evolved their sex cells independently of those of animals. In the

lower plants, both in the sea and in fresh water, the male
cells are motile, with two whiplike flagella extending from
the side; the female cells are like the smallest eggs of
animals, although distinctively plant. And just as much as
the sex cells of animals, the plant cells were designed to
live and unite in water. In short it is this: sperm, whether
of plant or animal, are small cells designed to swim through
water to find an egg. It was one of the earliest rules laid
down and it has led to complications ever since.

Frogmen are rediscovering the marine world at first hand.
It is harder to enter the ancient world of vegetation, for it
means journeying into time, not space. Yet it is there to be
found. We enter a realm of dampness, where only ferns
and mosses, mare's-tails and liverworts belong—plants that
produce spores but not seeds, that have no flowers and cannot reach very far for water. These still survive to the
present time, but when the coal forests were forming there
was little else.

Liverworts give you an idea of how things started, and
they also show that the life cycle of a plant is different from
an animal's. Two different generations alternate with each
other, one sexual and one that is not. Most liverworts are
small, ribbon-like plants that lie flat on damp soil, with an
upper surface designed to guard against loss of water and
a lower surface that takes water in. In a warm and misty
world you can see how it would matter very little if such
plants as these grew in or out of water along the margin
of a lake or swamp. In a sense they are actually no more or
less than half in and half out, and their reproductive
processes take advantage both of air and water. Each small
green ribbon produces a spore that needs only to reach damp
soil to start growing: it is not an egg and therefore sex

and fertilization have nothing to do with it. Yet at certain seasons the flat little plants that have grown from the spores produce disks which yield either eggs or sperm. The eggs need to be fertilized, and the sperm are swimming sperm that cannot move except in water. And, being plants, the parents of these sex cells cannot move to help them. Only when drenching rains fall and splash upon miniature forests of the two sexes mixed together do the sperm have a chance of reaching their objective.

In evolution one thing always leads to another and apparently little liverworts led the way to ferns and the tree

Sexual and nonsexual generations of a fern.

63

ferns that composed the large carboniferous forests—the first green canopy of the earth. To a great extent it is a shift in emphasis. The flat green liverworts produce either male or female cells, and in this respect are like an animal species with separate sexes. The fertilized egg grows into a little spore-producing plant anchored to the parent that produced the egg, and when ripe this plant bursts and casts its spores into the air above. The ferns do much the same but on a larger scale—and the first forests this earth has seen developed the new without losing the old.

The spore-producing generation grew larger and larger, and more complex, until some kinds became giant tree ferns one hundred feet high, casting their spores by never ending millions into the surrounding air. The ferns that are left to us still do the same, and in summertime most of us have seen the spore patches on the undersurface of the fronds. Cannel coal that burns with so much yellow flame consists entirely of tree-fern spores that settled, layer after layer, without germinating, on the swampy floor of those ancient forests. This gives us some measure of their number.

All this may seem remote from sex, but in reality it is not. The spore of a fern or of any other spore-producing plant is a reproductive unit of microscopic size. It shows with almost startling clarity that, given suitable conditions, any tiny fragment of an organism, if not too specialized, can grow into a whole one, although not necessarily like the old. For these fern spores are sexless—they are cells with the capacity to grow and develop, but they are neither eggs nor sperm. They spread the species, multiply its numbers, but all with a uniform sameness. And their purpose appears to be to compensate for the immobility of the parent plant, which, unlike animals, or most of them, remains rooted to

64

a spot. A frog can hop back to water to lay its eggs, but a fern cannot; and spores drifting through the air has been the answer. The spore does not need water in bulk but it does need moisture, and when one falls by chance where conditions are good, it develops, not into a fern or tree fern, but into something like a liverwort—flat, green and anchored to the ground by tiny hairlike processes which absorb water. It is heart-shaped and small, rarely over half an inch across, and develops sex organs but not spores. Unlike the liverworts, which are of two kinds, each with its own sex, this sexual generation of the fern produces both sexes— female, egg-producing structures at the crotch of the heart and sperm-producing structures at the point; hermaphrodites in fact. The world of the ferns reverts for a time from three to two dimensions, and the flagellated sperm swim through the thin film of water that is commonly present on the surface of the soil. In the days of emergence it could be counted upon.

The fern eggs that get fertilized develop in place and tall ferns grow up to produce spores in their turn—airborne, sexless but potent reproductive cells alternating with the eggs and sperm of the other generation.

Obviously reproduction by means of spores cast through the air and by sperm swimming to eggs through ground surface films of water is no more than a halfway stage in emancipation from an aquatic life. And so in the course of time the coal forests of tree ferns gave way to the less thirsty cover of conifers.

This is a remarkable transformation, simply in terms of the processes of reproduction, for it concerns the creation of the seed and the pollen grain. How it took place I am not sure, although botanists have their ideas about it. The

65

picture is complex and confusing, and only the outcome is clear.

It is as though the two generations of the ferns became fused into one. Spores of a sort are still produced, but they are no longer set free and cast to the winds. They remain on the parent and there develop to become a second generation, which seem to be an integral part of the parent tree. This generation constitutes the seeds within the female cone, and each produces eggs that need to be fertilized in order to develop. Such is the female—and water no longer enters the scheme of things. The spore-producing tree produces resident spores that develop in their place and form their eggs within the structure of the cone. You get

Male and female cones of pine.

the impression of the plant throwing itself partly out of water and employing that part to haul the rest out to join it.

Sexes are separate in the conifers, whether pine or spruce or monkey puzzle, and pollen grains drift down from their cones in a golden shower, some of which fall into the female cones and "pollinate" them. What has happened to the sperm? They are still there—and the pollen grain is the spore that used to drift to the ground, there to develop into the small flat plant which produced the waterborne sperm. Now the spore, if it is to do anything at all, drifts into a female cone and develops there like a small parasitic plant, becoming a pollen tube which eats its way through the layers of tissue that surround the eggs. When it has grown in far enough the tip bursts and allows two sperm, no longer equipped with swimming flagella, to enter and fertilize an egg. Everything is up in the air, and sex and reproduction in relation to water is a thing of the past. The wind takes the place of water entirely, apart from the requirements of growth, and the land is clothed in the green mantle of vegetation that sets the stage for the animal kingdom.

The migration from the fresh water onto the land was the result of a peculiar combination of circumstances. It took place during age-long periods when lands were low and there were extensive inland seas, and the whole earth was warm. Skies were mostly overcast and the heavy air was steamy with the humid heat. Anything that was wet stayed wet whether it was in the water or out of it. Little evaporation took place because the air was already saturated with moisture. Aquatic plants or animals that strayed beyond the water's edge would hardly have known the difference. They remained damp enough to go on living and were blanketed from the deadly rays of the sun by the misty overcast. It was possible and safe to venture, figuratively dripping, onto the land—and for more than one hundred million years this was the way it was. There was time, aeons of it, for all sorts of things to happen, with little need to hurry the changes.

Where plants led the way the animals followed, and ages before the first quadruped left a footprint in the mud the ancestors of the insects, spiders, millipedes and centipedes emerged and went their way. The story is by no means clear, although parts of it are known. Scorpion-like creatures and millipedes walked on the soggy land almost as soon as there was any vegetation at all, however low and flat it may have been. And as the age of the steaming coal forests got under way, centipedes and insects already crawled or flew. They had the terrestrial world to themselves for time out of mind.

This is merely history of a kind, I know, but all these creatures who left the streams and swamps for the adjoining land faced much the same problems as did the emerging plants: how to make aquatic eggs serve their purpose out of water. Part of the answer was to make them larger so that what hatched out would be a miniature of the parent, able to live in the same place and eat the same kind of food, instead of first having to become some peculiar type of aquatic larva; and to encase them in a membrane or shell impermeable to water, so that no moisture would escape from the developing egg.

Yet this was only a part of the answer. Eggs need to be fertilized by spermatozoa, but a sperm can travel only in a liquid medium—only here is the advantage an animal has compared with a plant, when both are fully terrestrial: it can move to its mate and has no need to accomplish fertiliza-

68

tion haphazardly from a distance. Mating, in the sense of actual coupling, is the rule, and scorpions, spiders, insects and their less conspicuous kind must copulate by some means or another. For eggs must be fertilized within the female body—otherwise the sperm cannot live or move to carry out its function. You would think that an egg membrane tough enough and watertight enough to be effective would make fertilization quite impossible—but every insect egg case has a minute pore at one end through which a sperm can enter and initiate development.

Such were the beginnings of the world that is now familiar to us—but for the most part and for a long time it grew out of an interplay between the green vegetation and an uncountable host of creatures with at least three pairs of legs and mostly with two pairs of wings. Our own story comes later.

8. perfume, starlight

and melody

The air was full of flying insects long before the age of the coal forests came to an end, with dragonflies of three-foot wing span searching for prey and oversized cockroaches chewing up the vegetation. Their descendants are smaller. When conifers took the place of tree ferns the larger insects were gone, and to the reptiles that by this time were walking about the land insects would be no more than a possible source of food and perhaps an irritation. It has been the luck of lizards and men alike that insect bodies are so tangled up inside with their vital air tubes that they cannot grow to a size that is dangerous to our kind. The insect world and the world of men never really meet—they interweave in space and make a mutual nuisance of themselves, but not much more than that. Insects are small but their world is large and they outbreed us all the time; and there are more kinds of insects than all of the other animals on land and in the sea put together. We need to define success most carefully to be sure that it belongs to us.

People often ask what good is an insect? Butterflies are pretty, bees are useful, hornets and others are nasty or destructive. As far as that goes, what good is anything? Benjamin Franklin countered with the question: what good is a newborn babe? Your answer depends on what you think of the universe and your place within it. From our point of view some insects are useful but most are not. Yet why should we have such a point of view that is so utterly self-centered?

My own feeling, or belief if you prefer such an immovable word, is that the universe is one and its wholeness is all-pervading. I believe, with others, that energy and matter, mind, emotion and spirit are all qualities of whatever this universe is made of, and we separate them because our own consciousness has become aware of them one at a time. I think that wherever a planet exists that is congenial to life, life will evolve, if it has not done so already—not as a visitation from some other place, but as an inborn creation, so to speak, of the planet itself in the light of its sun. The various forms that life can take depend upon the details of the circumstances—and the particular conditions supplied by the evolving earth have led to the peculiar forms of life we see around us and in the mirror. We are all earth-created creatures, with beauty and the love of life inborn in all that lives, from the lowest to the highest; our own uniqueness may lie in our awareness of it.

Life justifies its own existence. It flows through time in various channels, but all from a common source; insects have come along one path and we another—yet each finding that scent can be seductive, sounds alluring and light and color entrancing. What is mind and what is spirit I feel but do not know. Yet mind alone is a possession of many kinds

71

of creatures, each in its own degree. If life itself is the green shoot of the earth, mind and spirit are its flower. Most of the flowers are small but not necessarily insignificant because of that. One, the last to bloom, which is our own, is larger than any other. Yet all have their roots in the same ground, and none has been made for the benefit of another. Every kind of plant and animal on this planet I believe exists in its own right, each one is a novelty in the universe, a kind that has never before existed and never will again—and that is the essential tragedy when an organism becomes extinct. Some insects I like, most of them I do not. That is an individual and personal approach to lives of another sort. I detest mosquitoes and swat them when I can—there are plenty of them; but I know what I do and know I have no right to complain of their existence. Life takes life for one reason or another. All of them are selfish in the end.

Insects have eyes and a sense of smell, and some have a sense of hearing. It seems natural enough, for we have them too. Yet it should be startling, for out of an almost formless, senseless past, this sensory awareness has come into being quite independently in insects and in our own ancestral line.

Many insects have eyes of a remarkable efficiency, though not of the kind we have, and not all have good vision; others can make distinctive sounds and hear them as well; but all insects, so far as I know, have a well-developed sense of smell, located mainly in their antennae—freely movable processes projecting outward from the head.

Putting yourself in the place of another is never easy. I find it difficult if not impossible to see life, for instance, from the point of view of an untarnished Australian aboriginal; yet we are both men, of the same kind and size

72

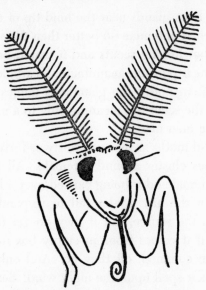

Insect head, with organs for taste,
sight, and long-distance smell.

of organism, walking about on the two-dimensional surface of the earth, and it shouldn't be too hard. But insects are small and generally have wings; freedom of movement is in three dimensions and space is relatively enormous; they might well live in another world.

Insects lay eggs that are protectively encased. Sexes are separate. And the problem of finding a mate at the right time and place is acute. Most of the larger moths depend upon their sense of smell to find their partners, sometimes from a distance that is hard to believe. This is particularly true of the emperor moths and their allies, many hawk moths and others; the males of all of these have branched or feathered antennae with increased surface and improved receptive quality. The males alone do the hunting.

The females remain seated and diffuse their scent into the

73

soft night air from glands near the hind tip of the body and have unbranched antennae no better than they need. These are the true bewitching scents and it would be an interesting experiment if perfume manufacturers would make them up and sell them under the glamorous names they like to use. Perhaps the scent has meaning only to a moth, perhaps it would drive men mad.

In the case of moths as many as thirty or forty eager males may sometimes cluster around a female. All the evidence points to the female odor being carried over a long distance by currents in the air. Males fail to respond if they are up-wind from the source, but if they do get the perfumed breeze, even if it comes from an empty box in which a female has been confined, off they go. And only virgins are able to cast their spell upon the night wind. Sex is pure and undefiled.

On occasion males liberated three miles away from a female have been known to find her, although the hunting might well be at random until the trail is picked up, perhaps five hundred yards away. Yet some males liberated a mile away have found their target within ten to twelve minutes and must have followed the line from the start. It is a good performance and a well-timed one as well, for each species of moth has its own hour for flight, a definite period in every twenty-four hours when they are on the wing and mating occurs.

Males have scent glands, too, which appear to stimulate the female and prepare her for mating, in some cases even causing her to do the hunting. The ghost moth is one of these. The glistening white raiment of the male helps to betray his presence as he hovers around in the darkness on rapidly beating wings, shedding his masculine aroma to

74

Butterflies mating.

draw the female to him as she flies among the grasses in search of him. The giant lacewing is another, although all he does is to sit about and spray the air around—it works every time, like the smell of tweeds and pine-scented soap at twilight. We have almost lost our own sense of smell, but what is left is powerful—a scent is either perfume or it stinks to high heaven, and a little generally goes a long way.

Dusk is a bewitching time, and other signs than scent are found within it—the winking lights of fireflies and the steady radiance of glowworms, depending on which continent you stand on. Shelley wrote of "the glowworm golden, shedding unbeholden its aerial hue"—although it is not unbeholden, for all who have seen the green lamps glowing in the hedge-

75

rows and downlands of England or elsewhere have caught
their breath. They are the lamps of elf land and you cannot pass them by. And even when no human is there to see
them on a summer night, they are seen by those they shine
for. The lady has a light in her window and the young men
come calling.

Most animals and plants have been assigned a Latin name,
two of them in fact, and most such names have no more
meaning than yours or mine and sound outlandish to the
ear. But the glowworm has a pair that I like—*Lampyris
noctiluca*—meaning, if we do not inquire too closely, the
fire flame night light.

Only the female glows: a wingless beetle that occupies a
permanent position on the ground night after night advertiz-
ing her receptive presence to the lampless males flying
through the dark. Sometimes males are attracted to her in
hundreds, although any small light may be mistaken by
them, and I have had too many of them come into a lighted
tent at night—as drab and unpleasing as small cockroaches.
Only the realization of the compliment intended has made
me look upon them with a more kindly eye. You don't often
in this life get mistaken for a glowworm.

Another living lamp lives in tropical America and goes by
the name of railroad worm. It sounds like the glowworm
again, with a more elaborate lighting system, although less
is known concerning its sexual lure. The male is a large
typical beetle with no definite luminosity, but the adult female, which like the female glowworm has no wings, and
the young of both sexes, have the most remarkable of all
living lights. They emit a greenish-yellow flash from eleven
well-spaced spots along each side of the body, like the
lighted compartments of a train; while a bright red head-

light glows from the front of the head. Sometimes all and sometimes only some of the greenish lights are turned on, and sometimes the red lamp glows alone.

It is one way, and perhaps a compensation, for keeping the female in her place. If she has no wings to permit her to fly away and wander far afield, and has to stay more or less at home, a light in the darkness is the least she should have. In actuality these wingless females are sexually mature adolescents—their ovaries and egg-laying apparatus matures but their bodies never grow up except in size and the adult insect never appears. Only the males complete their development and, having wings, must do all the searching for a mate.

The female tussock moth grows in caterpillar form until all growth is over, climbs up a tuft of grass, spins a cocoon and eventually transforms herself into a wingless moth not much more advanced than the glowworm. Only the males take wing. The female sits upon the remains of her cocoon, casting her perfume to the winds until her partner finds her. Then she lays her eggs upon the cocoon and dies. The silkworm moths behave the same. And in a way it is the story of the sex cells repeated in terms of air instead of water. An appointment between two partners is easier to keep if one of them remains under a lamp or a rosebush while the other does the searching. In the end, it saves a lot of time.

Even then a system of signaling can help a lot and the dancing lights of the fireflies on summer evenings is a case in point. I have had few experiences that have brought home to me so sharply the feeling of being a trespasser in another world, as watching the fireflies begin to flash under the trees when the sun's afterglow has almost gone. You feel like a blundering giant on an exquisitely beautiful but alien earth, as if what you are watching was never meant for you to see. Which, of course, is true enough. It is their world that we have taken.

Fireflies flash, I suppose, because light signals can be more precise and effective than scent—and because there is a general tendency for light to be produced by living tissue, from bacteria to fish. Many forms have found it useful. And wherever it turns up, the essential chemistry of the process is the same—a reaction akin to a process of digestion; light is produced as a by-product, but there is very little heat. It is as cold a light as its color suggests. Little glands produce the light, often with reflectors at the back to direct its rays, and like any other gland comes under nervous control. A flash can be sent out or not, according to the circumstances.

Both male and female fireflies emerge from the grass at dusk and the males fly about, emitting a single flash at intervals. The female climbs up a blade of grass and perches there. As a rule she doesn't fly at all although, unlike the glowworm, she is equipped to do so; and she never flashes spontaneously—the male must wink first.

If a male flashes within three or four yards of a female she usually responds, after pulling herself together, by flashing back. He then turns directly toward her in his course and glows again, to which she again responds; and after exchanging signals not more than five or ten times the male reaches the female and mates with her.

Males rarely respond to flashes from other males, in the common firefly at least, and recognition of the right kind of female—for there are several firefly species about—depends upon the time-interval between the flash of the male and that of the female. If she is too quick or too slow in

78

her response she isn't the girl he is looking for. Yet the interval between the flashes and the duration of the flash itself, in combination, is distinctive for each species, and the system appears to work beautifully in every sense of the word.

What is born of necessity may grow into art for art's sake alone. A signaling system in which a female flashes in response to a male after a definite time-interval can easily lead to simultaneous flashing of males in response to one female —you see it on street corners all the time. And once in a while you can see group flashing among North American fireflies. Yet it is rare; the real displays of flashing are seen among the tropical fireflies of southeast Asia and the adjacent islands.

Early travelers in Siam were particularly impressed by the firefly display. It still is, in fact, one of the sights of the Far East—in Burma, Siam, the Philippines and the Indonesian archipelago. In these regions all the fireflies on one tree will flash, for example, one hundred times a minute in perfect unison; while on another tree not far away the same degree of unison will be kept, although out of step with the first. And all the fireflies on the trees are males which have flown out from the jungle; the whereabouts of the females are unknown. The synchronous flashing may be kept up hour after hour, night after night, for weeks or even months, whether there is a dead calm or a steady wind, a clear night, overcast, or even rain. Only in the bright moonlight does it die down—the greater light, like that of the sun, overwhelms them. What is at first a sexual purpose here seems to serve no useful end, and recalls the drinking song "the more we get together the happier we will be." Who can say that there is no element of communal satisfaction and enjoyment

79

of performance and living in such male communities of the insect world? The light is seen, the rhythm is sensed whether or not we as humans are there to appreciate it. The nightly dance of the fireflies exists, and it is worth thinking about.

There is one other luminous insect that merits notice. The so-called lantern fly, a large insect of tropical South America, has a large, elongated head which luminesces when its owner is in flight and searching for a breeding partner. Both sexes fly, and each individual has a bright light which can be switched on and off, and is kept continuously alight only when the two sexes are aware of each other's proximity. The light comes on only late at night—and it is no wonder that the natives report seeing ghosts.

Flashing lights and seductive scents are designed for employment at night. The light and the winds of daytime are too strong for their use. But sound can be used as a signal by day and by night as well, as long as sound itself can be heard.

Grasshoppers, crickets, katydids and cicadas attract their mates with song, or the nearest to singing an insect can manage. Even the harmless male mosquito finds his blood-sucking mate in the dark by the hum she makes with her fast-beating wings—sensing the sound with his plumy antennae. Yet no insect has a true voice and the sound is usually made by stridulating—rubbing one hard part against another, using legs, wings and body in various ways according to the species. The sound produced by each is distinctive and serves to bring the sexes together, although only the males produce the noise, as you might expect. After all, if a predatory bird locates a noisy male cicada whirring away in a tree top, no eggs are lost, and the silent female lives to mate another day. Males are expendable. Females are not.

The sounds vary greatly. W. H. Hudson wrote of the intrinsic beauty of the sounds of the field cricket and of the coarser, creaky notes of the house cricket, and even thought that the penetrating song of the great green grasshopper was music, that the males expressed their rivalry in their singing, a sort of contest rather than a means of attracting the female. The males of these grasshoppers commence their stridulations just before sundown and continue far into the night, using the same perches on a twig or an ear of wheat, night after night. Mole crickets start up at about the same time, with a low, dull jarring note, continuing for a long time without interruption.

Noise, of course, whether pleasing or not, has meaning only to those that can hear—and hearing is a sense associated almost exclusively with air waves. Crickets and katydids have their pair of hearing organs in the lower joint of the forelegs; grasshoppers have theirs in the sides of the abdomen, and cicadas have theirs in much the same place. Both sexes are able to hear. But the vast majority of the horde of insects are deaf and dumb and live in a silent world that would seem to us to be but half alive.

The males make the noise when it is made at all, and thereby may advertise themselves to danger; but the females are the ones that have to search for their mates which, I suppose, is only fair. They can be fooled too: when individuals of different sexes of field crickets and longhorned grasshoppers are kept entirely apart, in different rooms far out of ordinary sound range for one another, a microphone placed among the males and connected with an earphone in the cage of females causes the ladies to move with active antennae towards the microphone. A phonograph record of the notes of the males has the same summoning effect. Music is evocative even when the broadcast is delayed.

And so by sound, by smell, by touch, by sight, the search goes on to find a mate and reproduce, among all the creeping and flying multitudes whose kind were the first to dwell upon the land.

9. the mating of flowers

This is an interacting universe and it seems to me that few things show it so clearly as flowers and the animals which pollinate them. The making and mating of a flower has gone hand in hand with the evolutionary refinements of insects and of certain birds and mammals. Left alone to the sun and the wind, plants would never have evolved a flower as we know it, although our knowing and liking a flower has had nothing to do with it. Yet beauty, it is said, lies only in the eyes of the beholder—a half-truth if there ever was one—but it seems pretty certain that if insects had no eye for color, flowers would be without it. And if insects had no need of help in their unwitting services to the plant, flowers would not have the form they have. But it is not all insect. The beauty of symmetry is there, and no matter how far insects have called it forth, it is in itself the inborn rhythm of growth.

Flowers, apart from the seeds they bear, are accessory organs of reproduction as surely as the tail of a peacock, although their meaning was a mystery until two centuries ago. For where a cock has need to display to stimulate a hen, plants stand rooted where their roots sink down and their reproductive need is to exploit some go-between.

83

We need to go back to the age of conifers when all the forests were coniferous evergreens and beetles and reptiles dominated the animal world on land—a world of monotonous color and no song, a time when there were no birds, no butterflies, no mammals and no flowers to speak of. It seems somewhat dull and, when you think of beetles and dinosaurs as the best life could offer, rather horrible. Yet all that we have and are has come from that.

The plants of the age of conifers and reptiles were of separate sexes and depended upon the wind for pollination. Cross-fertilization was the rule, but the wind is never reliable and the pollen dust that must be shed to be effective is beyond imagination. In some, the pollen grains had wings to help them on their drifting flight. The eggs or seeds, in cones or on leaves, exuded drops of sap to trap what came their way.

The first flowers were beetle flowers and this seems to have been the beginning. Beetles feeding on the sap and resin of stems and leaves must have discovered that the liquid droplets from the male and female cones were odoriferous and nourishing—and some, returning regularly to feed on them, accidentally carried pollen to the eggs. And so it started. From this point on, as insects became more and more diversified, the flower came into being as a central stigma for the collection of pollen grains leading down to deep-seated eggs, surrounded by stamens for delivering pollen for the insect to take away to another flower. We can only speculate on how the changes came and I doubt that it is very profitable as yet for us to do so—beetle pollination may have brought the plant sexes together to become the hermaphrodite beetle flower, or this may have been the state of affairs from the beginning. It is hard to

84

tell and we may never know. Yet the fact remains that beetle flowers are still the most primitive flowers we have.

The beetle flowers that still survive are most abundant in the tropics, and they attract their insect pollen-carriers by offering smells of the kind they like. The beetles are beetles and have not changed because of plants—they go their ancient way and feed on sap, fruit, leaves and the remains of any animals they find. They live in an aromatic world where sight is of less importance than odor. One group of beetle flowers has large, solitary blossoms and includes magnolias, pond lilies, California poppy and the wild rose; the other has clusters of smaller ones, like dogwood, elder and buckthorn. The beetles not only lap up nectar and other juices but feed upon the petals and stamens, and, to protect their eggs from the jaws of their pollinators, most beetle flowers keep them well below the floral crown. Most of them are primitive—they are large, bright and heavily scented, it seems, because the low-slung beetles have a sense of color and smell.

From here, we go on. In a changing world, cross-fertilization or cross-pollination has been necessary to produce progeny variable enough to cope with changing circumstances, and plants have had as much need of it as animals. And, without delving into history, we can see the wind again in trees of more modern kinds—in the catkins of the oak and birch, hazel and poplar, hanging so that the wind can blow their pollen far and wide. The female flower, if we can call the inconspicuous reproductive units by that colorful name, grows on the same tree as the male but not in the same place and opens at a slightly different time. The tree combines the sexes, but not in a single flower,

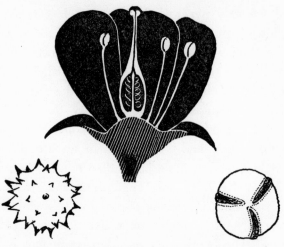

Anatomy of flower, showing central female pistil and ovary, and three male stamens; also two examples of pollen grains.

which may be something old. Yet flowers by and large combine the sexes: a central pistil with pollen-receptive stigma at the top and eggs or ovules hidden in its base—the female unit; a ring or rings of stamens, bearing pollen-producing anthers, surrounding it—the male unit; and outer rings of leaflike protective structures, which may or may not be glorified as brightly colored petals, around the whole. Such is the flower in general, and its problems usually are two—how to become fertilized by pollen from another plant, and how to avoid becoming fertilized by its own.

Cross-fertilization produces a much wider range of variation among the offspring of either plants or animals, and it is this variety which is the raw material upon which natural selection works to bring about changes in the course of many generations. Where adaptability is all-important, this is essential. It may also be essential when the perfect type, so to speak, is hard to fix upon, and natural selection by external agencies may be relied on to weed out the progeny that are too different from their parents one way or another. Most animals depend upon it for either change or security, and inbreeding can be, but is not necessarily, dangerous. The point is that where there is any weakness in the stock, inbreeding intensifies it, while outbreeding may mask it.

But, in a very large number of flowering plants, strains have been evolved in the course of great periods of time that are more or less stabilized, and self-pollination has become substituted for cross-pollination. Grasses, for instance, are very well adapted to cross-pollination by the wind, yet many of them, including wheat, oats and barley, pollinate themselves. This is easily managed. The anthers simply burst before they are extruded from the flower and the trick is done—the wind is too late. A few flowers have gone even further and skip pollination altogether: the dandelion, for all its yellow invitation, sets seed without fertilization of any kind, whether from itself or from another plant. It is sub-sexual in the same sense as the summer broods of water fleas. The result is a plant that is wonderfully well suited to living in abundance in the places where you expect to see it. But it would have a harder time than most in adapting to a new set of circumstances.

Cross-pollination or cross-fertilization is still the rule, however, for the great majority, and many are the ways for ensuring it and avoiding the alternative. Some plants simply cannot self-pollinate—the dahlia is one of them. The pollen will not germinate on the stigma of a flower on the same plant.

In the end, as in the beginning, we need to turn to the

87

animal kingdom, for unless we regard the flower as being no more than a circle of male stamens surrounding the female pistil, or groups of these clustered together, there is no sense to it. Its shape and color and size, all in fact that catches your eye and makes you catch your breath as well, is something added—and is there to attract and perhaps to force an insect or even a bird or a bat to bring to it pollen from another plant and take away some of its own. Darwin recognized this long ago and wrote a book about it. And so there are bee flowers and moth flowers, fly flowers and beetle flowers, and the bird flowers and bat flowers—all different from those of the wind.

How much of this is sex or reproduction, I am not sure, but this animal-vegetable relationship I think is fascinating, and demands attention.

Bee flowers include violets and verbena, some orchids, blue columbine, larkspur, monkshood, bleeding heart, many members of the snapdragon, mint and pea families and a host of others. You can add to the list as you will on any balmy summer day. They are all showy, with brightly colored petals, sweetly fragrant, and all offer nectar to the bees that come to them. The colors are mostly blue or yellow, or combinations of them, to conform to the color vision of the bee—for bees see a color range from yellow into the ultra-violet and are color blind to red. Bees like sweet or minty odors and fly only by day—and so the flowers are scented likewise and usually close at night. The bee settles on the flower and the long bee tongue dips deeply to the base of the tube of petals where the nectar lies, where most other insects cannot reach, picks up pollen on its body hairs unknowingly, and flies quickly to another flower of the same kind if possible. Pollen is brought and other pollen picked up, and each kind of bee is suited to its own group of flowers—or perhaps it is better put the other way, for while bumblebees do not depend on monkshood for their living, monkshood cannot get along without the bumblebee and is limited to its range. Without bees of all sorts to pollinate their flowers, one hundred thousand species of plants or more would perish from the earth. It seems to me a heavy responsibility for one kind of insect to have to carry.

Moths and butterflies also have their flowers, each with its own characteristics. Moth flowers are morning glory, yellow columbine, tobacco, yucca, phlox, evening primrose and many orchids. Moths do not settle upon the flowers

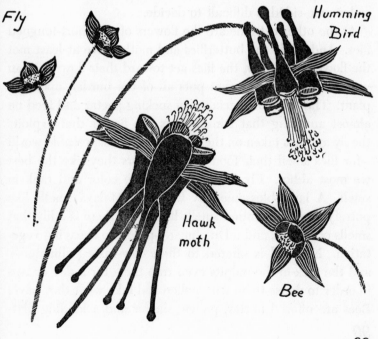

Fly

Humming Bird

Hawk moth

Bee

they suck but hover above them and lower their long tongues into the nectar—in tropical hawk moths they are sometimes ten inches long. Both sight and smell guide the moths, but since most of them fly during dusk or night the flowers run mainly to shades of white and to heavy fragrance; they are open in late afternoon or evening and stay closed during the day. Butterflies fly by day and it is then their flowers are open, and since, unlike the bees, a butterfly sees color well into the red, butterfly flowers tend to red and orange. And in both moth and butterfly flowers the nectar lies at the base of a long, slender, tubular spur, and there is a close matching of the length of the spur and the length of the tongue of the moth or butterfly that visits that particular flower. The fitting of tongue to spur holds insect and flower together, but whether the fitting is mutual or more or less one-sided is difficult to decide.

At the other extreme are the flowers of the short-tongued flies. And while the butterflies and moths have at least met the flowers part way, the flies act toward their flowers in an unskilled, stupid way that puts all of the burden upon the plant. They do not specialize in sucking nectar and feed on almost anything that stinks. It is the flower that exploits the fly and has taken on the quality of its disagreeable world —for flies smell their food and the odors they like the best we most abhor. Fly flowers are dull in color and rank in smell. A large-blossomed fly flower in Malaya smells like putrefying flesh, another smells like dung; there is a lily that smells of fish oil, and a Dutchman's-pipe like decaying vegetation. No food is offered to these low-caste pollinators— and the jack-in-the-pulpits even trap them for a day or two in order to douse them with pollen and take what they have. Bees are offered nectar, pollen, shelter and a landing platform, fragrance and bright colors; for flies there is only trouble, pitfalls, prisons and false allures!

Flowers have taken advantage, I was going to say, of birds and bats as well as bees; but, when reward is commensurate with the service, the advantage is mutual—you feel that nature broods upon the scene and pronounces magic words upon the visitor and visited.

Birds have powerful vision toward the red but not the blue, and have a poor sense of smell—you can almost guess the rest. Their flowers are red and yellow: red columbine, fuchsia, passion flower, hibiscus, and many cacti, orchids and others. Hummingbirds suck on the wing and favor the hanging types, the sunbirds of Africa and Asia do not and their flowers usually stand erect and provide a landing platform. Seeds are kept well out of harm's way from the beak, behind the floral parts, and petals are fused to form a tube which holds large amounts of thin nectar. The nectar tube often matches the length and curvature of the beak of the bird, while stamens are arranged so that they brush against its breast. The Mexican century plant lives only where humming birds can pollinate it. Its dependence is complete.

Bees, butterflies and birds seem to go naturally with flowers—but not a bat. Bats go out at night and see but poorly. Yet as birds and butterflies belong to daylight and color, bats and moths have the night and smell. Bat flowers are pollinated by certain tropical bats equipped with long slender snouts, protrudable tongues and shortened or missing front teeth, all of which fit them to feed on the flowers. In going from flower to flower, they carry the pollen. The flowers, which are tropical, are large and mostly white, open only at night and attract the bats by giving off a fermenting or fruitlike odor; the calabash, candle-tree and areca palm are among them.

Color dominates the scene around us and I think is what pleases us most. Yet we take it for granted. It is there to see—in flowers and butterflies and birds—but we didn't put it there and are only now beginning to realize how lucky we are that we can see it. For as far as we know, among the mammals, only the anthropoids have color vision. We and the apes and monkeys see color; moreover where else in the mammalian group can you find such colorful creatures as the blue-faced mandrill? The rest of the warm-blooded hairy folk apparently are color blind. They are drab enough to prove it.

Yet the colors we admire so much in the living world are there because the insects as a whole know one color from another. This we know—but the circumstantial evidence is there in any case. Flowers are colored primarily because insects exist that see color and make use of it. And the most colorful of insects—the butterflies—are colored in various ways for various reasons. One of these is sex and their own color vision; another is related to the fact that birds see color, too, and feed upon the insects. A butterfly needs to feed and mate; it also needs to avoid being eaten. And by playing both ends of the color scheme, the insect avoids a compromise.

The brightly colored upper surfaces of the wings of butterflies appear to be advertisements which bring notice of one insect to another, and the males locate their females by the colors and not by scent—although both vision and sense of smell may vary greatly among these insects, and what may be true of many may not be true of all. Yet butterflies have their enemies, especially among the birds, and color informs predators as well as prospective mates. So the under surface of the wings, which is all that shows when the insect is at rest, is camouflaged in brownish break-up patterns which hide it from the bird; and in many forms the upper vivid surface may be over-bright as a warning that its owner has a bitter taste and is best left alone, or has decoy bands or eyespots that draw the fatal thrust away from vital centers. Sex flaunts its color when it can, but it is often unsafe to do so—and only plants appear to display it with impunity.

10. sex and societies

Human society is complex and unstable—which makes living in it interesting, irritating and hopeful. It is essentially a society created and run by males, something most women and some men regret. And it is a society not merely in its childhood but in its drooling though destructive infancy, too young in fact to have had any history in the real sense of the word—a few thousand years, two or three hundred generations at the most. It has no antiquity, and the remarkable thing about it is that so much has happened in such a short time. Our society is based on an evenly balanced sex ratio, with males and females produced in approximately equal numbers, and with all individuals of both sexes fully developed.

The insects must have started in much the same way, with separate sexes produced in equal numbers and no more of a society anywhere than in the meeting and mating of a pair. Yet, insects have been insects for several hundred million years, and they have had organized societies for fifty to a hundred million years at least. Their societies are as old as the hills, conservative and enduring, and are based on the control of sex and growth. We cannot afford to take them lightly while we climb the social ladder.

94

Societies have arisen a number of times: among wasps and bees, ants and termites. In most, if not all, cases they depend upon a reproductive capacity of individual females that is startling, to say the least. And I think we need to distinguish between sex and reproduction. Reproduction may be more or less independent of sex, and sex may concern more the nature of the individuals than their number. Certain wasps show this clearly.

The eggs of chalcid wasps, for instance, which are so small they are laid within the eggs of moths and other insects, undergo a kind of multiplication called polyembryony. The moth egg hatches into a caterpillar and starts its meandering existence with the wasp egg already growing inside. In such a place the growth runs wild, the wasp egg seems to forget itself and grows into a sausage-shaped mass of cells which divides up into a chain of separate embryos. And only as the juices of the caterpillar begin to run dry does the process stop. Each unit comes to itself, develops according to pattern into a grub and, finally, into another little wasp. According to the species, fifty or even a thousand identical wasps may arise from the single original egg. It is reproduction with a vengeance—the same individual repeated over and over again with no variation at all.

Gall wasps and the sawflies so destructive to the forests do not go so far or employ the same means, but the idea is much the same. They have found a certain way of life with almost unlimited scope just as long as the trees last, and their chief racial concern is to produce as many individuals of one kind as possible, all capable of reproducing in turn. It is all too easy. The male sex is eliminated. All eggs develop by parthenogenesis into females, and generation after generation it goes on. Theoretically, I suppose there should

95

come a time when circumstances cause males to reappear, as they do in the water fleas, but so far not one has been seen. Purely female lines have become established, every individual breeds more females like itself, variation among them is reduced to a minimum, the insects flourish and the forests suffer. By itself a female tribe produces extraordinary numbers, but it conserves the pattern of the species and does not encourage change.

This is reproduction carried to its extreme, designed to take advantage of unusual opportunities for growth. The insect societies are more than this. There are many kinds and, altogether, an organized society has come into being about thirty different times during the long insect history. Like our own, they start with the mating of a male and female and the growing up of the offspring under the care of one or both parents. You can see where we stand. The paths lie open before us, and those the insects took may or may not be the ones we want to take.

In the case of insects a more or less permanent family is formed of enormous size, either through the production of successive generations of offspring by the same mother or through numbers of mothers of sister-sister relationship remaining together with their progeny alongside. The societies are not so much female as they are maternal. Some are small and loosely held together, but others may be very large and stable—the ants, honeybees, social wasps, and termites. In all of these the individuals are very highly integrated with one another—individuality counts for almost nothing, the state is all. The social division of labor is so sharp that castes are produced which serve different functions, such as workers or soldiers or reproductives. The detailed patterns of the societies lead us too far astray, and

96

for the present I am concerned with the mechanisms involved. For while the various castes are connected with food-getting and communal defense, the main activities of any insect colony center in reproduction, that is, in producing and rearing as many young as possible.

In the case of bees we are taken deep within the hive. I have watched bees coming and going to their flowers and I have robbed them of their honey, but the point of interest here is what goes on inside the queen bee as she lays her eggs. It is the private business of the queen but it controls the nature and the future of the colony, and is a matter of sex control.

The queen mates once and for all on her nuptial flight and has a sperm sac filled with sperm. It is all she has or will ever get. As eggs pass from the ovary along the oviduct to be laid, sperm pass through the narrow sperm sac tube to join them. The opening of this tube is controlled by a ring of muscle, and it can be closed or opened under the influence of a nerve. Such is the essential machinery. It is simple enough, and this is the way it works.

All through the summer the eggs pass along and each receives its sperm. Fertilized bee eggs all have the double dose of the sex component and develop into females. If well fed, such offspring become fully grown and sexually mature, queens in fact. If reared on a reducing diet their growth is stunted and they live out their lives as workers—undersized, sterile females. The system is fine as long as the productive season lasts, but sooner or later a change comes over the queen. Whether it comes from the feel or sight of the brood cells in the hive, or something akin to loneliness, or a feeling of climatic or seasonal change, I have no idea.

97

At any rate, in late summer the number of drone-producing eggs greatly increases.

Perhaps the pressure of sperm in the partly emptied sperm sac falls below a certain threshold for effectiveness, or perhaps the lady feels her age and suffers from a nervous tension that keeps the sperm duct closed. Whatever it is, it works. Each egg that passes by without getting fertilized still manages to develop, but with only the single unit of the sex agent each such egg becomes a male—a drone. The switchover is not complete, and it is a co-operative venture between the queen and workers. She lays the unfertilized drone eggs in the relatively large drone cells made ready by the worker bees, and lays the fertilized eggs in other cells, one or more of which will be fed well enough to grow into a queen. The stage is set for making a new colony, not merely the continued growth of the original one.

Bee swarming begins and its essence is reproduction of the community as a community. The reigning, fertilized queen leaves together with a large number of workers; the original colony becomes dominated by a new queen which the workers have guarded from attacks by her predecessor. Being a virgin, she also leaves the colony on her marriage flight, but after a midair mating returns to the hive. When she takes off, a crowd of eager males pursues her, which ensures that one at least will catch her. This makes it certain, too, that the successful drone will be a strong-flying insect and no stunted cripple with imperfect wings. The drones may not have much to do, but the one that mates with the queen and plays a full part in the production of the future queens and workers must have his inheritance in perfect shape. That one male becomes all-important, like a prize pedigree bull.

98

Nuptial flight of a pair of ants.

Ants and termites are somewhat different, though they carry the caste system further than the bees. Ants swarm on certain days in summertime and I have always been amazed to see them creeping out of the cracks in the ground among the pine and spruce needles, emerging from below the spreading roots. When the day is right, they seem to issue from the ground all through the woods. At times the air has been so thick with the flying queens and males that I have wished I were indoors. Their numbers stagger you and so does the uncanny timing of the emigration. What is the signal that tells them now is the time to go forth, all who are able, and start new colonies wherever possible?

Mating occurs in the air. Is it a relic of ant flights of long ago or a means of keeping the insect a perfect insect even though wings are not wanted underground? Once mating is over, the male is finished and lives but a short while alone in the world. The female lives long and starts her colony by herself without the aid of a worker retinue.

As soon as she lands, with her sperm sac full of sperm and the duct closed tight, she casts off her wings. They have been used for the first and last time, and now in a solitary confinement of her own making the female waits while her eggs grow to the proper size for laying. Why they are not already grown I do not know—perhaps an ant flies better or farther without their weight—but the great wing muscles, now no longer needed, break up and nourish the growth of the eggs. It is weeks or months before they ripen, but at last wingless workers hatch from them and the colony is founded.

In the case of bees, the sex cells alone determine whether males or females are produced, depending on whether or not the eggs are fertilized; but whether a female egg develops into a queen or a worker depends on how other workers feed the grub that hatches. Society is based on both sex and diet.

In ants and termites the control lies within the ovary itself, and it has been gained independently by them, for ants and termites are not at all closely related. As in the bee, all fertilized eggs are destined to be females. Yet the ripe eggs do not always leave the ovary as soon as they are grown. Those that do and are fertilized as they pass along, become queens; those that miss being fertilized become the males or kings. But the eggs that are slow in leaving the ovary become partly resorbed and are smaller when they leave, and according to their size become workers or soldiers, all of them sterilized and contentedly employed no matter what they look like.

100

It comes to this, in bees and ants and all other kinds of social insects, that the fertile female is the founder and the matriarch of the society. The problem of the male, which is a real one, has been solved and the societies are stabilized.

For obvious biological reasons the female is the social sex, while, generally speaking, the male throughout the animal kingdom is either unsocial or even anti-social. When the values of some social organization were discovered, as a new and powerful form of adaptation to environmental circumstances, the disruptive tendencies of the male became a nuisance. Female societies have evolved in which the males have been reduced to little more than a fertilizing agency, and in every other way, since they can't fit into the scheme of things, they are simply kept out. Bees tolerate a fair number of males as social parasites, as long as they do not get in the way. Ants need a lot of them once in a while, but they see to it that their lives are short. Termites go the farthest. The great queen who may lay her eggs at the rate of 30,000 a day for years on end is allowed one fully developed but virtually captive consort. Male unemployment is solved in the same way as overabundance of fertile females —by sterilization before development even starts. The societies are fully stabilized and fully evolved, with nowhere left to go—conservative, female, unchanging—the perfect states. Is it worth it?

11. more deadly than the male

Spiders repel me as they do most people. Why it should be so, I am not sure. Perhaps there are so many reasons no single one seems to be responsible. Even as a biologist I have kept my distance save for those unhappy occasions when a spider has taken me unawares. Yet, many naturalists have made spiders and their relatives the study of a lifetime. Henri Fabre appears to have had a passion for them, although his interest seems to have been more in some of their macabre activities than a real feeling for them, and E. B. White's sympathetic *Charlotte's Web* is the only story I know that made a spider my fellow creature.

When you think about it, spiders can no more help inheriting their peculiar looks and their lust for the juice of insects than we can for having to balance on our two hind legs. Spiders have grown into the world as they have found it and do the best with what they have and are: a trunk with four pairs of legs, a pendulous abdomen in the rear equipped with glands for spinning silk, a pair of sensory palps or feelers and

102

a pair of fangs in front, is most of it, at least as far as appearances go. If you look more closely you can see the eyes, six or eight of them variously arranged, a marvelous design for scanning in all directions at once. Sight should be the dominant sense. It is not. As an image-maker, each eye is about as poor as an eye can be, and the wonder is that a spider can distinguish anything besides the movement of an object within its range. And this extraordinary poverty of sight seems to condition almost everything a spider does, from sex to assassination.

Take sex alone, for instance. If only a female were a vegetarian or could recognize a gentle male at a glance, all would be so simple. But she is not. She is a half-blind savage carnivore, and this places the smaller male that has to mate with her in an exceedingly dangerous predicament. The male must be both agile and ingenious to effect a mating and escape alive. And still he has to do it or contribute to race suicide, for in spite of ancestral aquatic connections spiders are as fully terrestrial as anything that walks on land.

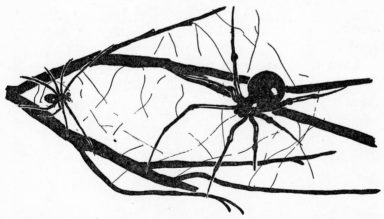

Black widow spider on web, with small male approaching.

Their eggs are comparatively large, at least sufficiently to hatch out as small spiders capable of acting as such, but the eggs, being enclosed in impermeable protective cases, must be fertilized within the body of the mother. As far as the male is concerned it is a question of do or die, or maybe both.

We know the world around us through our senses, and the universe overwhelms us through our eyes; sound may be music, a whisper in the night or an explosion; the air is scented or befouled; we know the taste of things and we know the touch; we know what we look like and our fingers have told us the solidity and the contours of our shape. And it took the years of our forgotten infancy to become aware of ourselves and our surroundings.

What does a spider have? Poor sight at the very best and generally much worse than that; no hearing—its world is silent as well as dim or dark; apparently, no smell of the kind that we and the insects have, sensing the breezes. It has taste and it has touch, two senses seemingly rolled into one. Like a man blind and deaf, a spider feels its way through life attuned to every contact with the enormous world about it. Under the circumstances, it is surprising that a spider should be a hunter or even a trapper.

Even in the country of the half-blind, some see better or worse than others. Jumping spiders and wolf spiders have keen sight—that is, for a spider. They can distinguish one object from another at a distance of nearly a foot, which seems to be the greatest extent of their blurry universe. The females hunt and catch their food and in due course lay up their eggs inside themselves. The males exist to fertilize the eggs no matter what the cost, yet even these prefer to live another day, perhaps to mate again. And that is the prob-

104

lem. The female must be disarmed either by force or by suggestion. Males that get eaten before they mate simply have failed in their duty. Afterward it doesn't matter so much; the tragedy becomes individual, not racial.

So, males do the best they can to live through the act of mating and, if possible, to survive it. The technique varies, but a little vision makes a lot of difference and it works both ways. The male has a chance to signal to the female from a fairly safe distance and yet be seen and recognized and, equally important, he can see her before he accidently bumps into her, an encounter that generally would be fatal.

Some of the wolf spiders take no chances. The male leaps at the female, mates without any preliminaries and then makes a dash for it—on the hit and run principle. It works all right for those that are quick enough, but a good many males must have contributed to their progeny by nourishing the mother instead of fertilizing her eggs. But other wolf spiders semaphore their presence or signal in some other way.

The flaglike palps of one little wolf are blackened and as soon as he sights the female his antics start. Standing on tiptoes, to be seen as clearly as possible, he extends his flags, one up and one down. Then they are withdrawn and re-

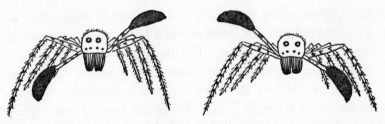

Male wolf spider semaphoring his identity to female.

Wolf spider swaying from side to side, "dancing," to signal his identity to female.

extended, one down and the other up; and each time, with quivering body, he takes a timid step forward. Others have one pair of black legs and all else light, and these lift the black pair up and down together. And still others sway drunkenly from side to side. It is courtship of a kind and the general effect upon the female is hypnotic. It takes whatever mind she has off hunger, and whether or not she becomes sexually aroused she becomes receptive and non-aggressive. In a spider way I suppose it is equivalent to plying the lady with drink.

Crab spiders have somewhat flattened, crab-shaped bodies and a sideways walk, and lie in wait for bees and other insects that visit flowers. I like them least of all, perhaps because a crab reminds me of a spider, and a spider that looks like a crab is a felony compounded. Fabre called his captive crab a little gem and was lost in admiration at the maternal care she lavished upon her eggs—it all depends upon your point of view. But the male knows his female and perhaps because of their flattened shape has discovered how to handle her. For once the male is dominant. As soon as he meets a female he climbs on her back at once, often to roll over and over with her before her struggles cease.

106

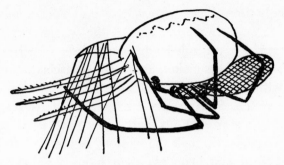

*Male spider mating with female after having secured
her to the ground by means of threads.*

And in some the male ties the female, before mating, to the
ground with so much silk she has a hard time getting free.
Rape is the rule, and in all of the animal kingdom only men
and male crab spiders appear to practice it. A man is known
by the company he keeps.

There is an Italian dance called the tarantella which is
supposed to have been inspired by the convulsive jerkings
of persons bitten by certain spiders, the tarantulas. Some
of them are common in the southwestern states, where they
live in colonies of twelve or more individuals. They are
larger and blinder than most spiders that actively hunt their
prey.

A tarantula on the prowl is like a blind, deaf wolf that
can trail its victim only by tasting the ground, not even sniff-
ing it. For this is what the hunting spider does. Its pair of
palps contain organs that combine simple touch and something like taste—you can feel it to some extent if you can
imagine your sense of taste transferred to your finger tips.
Yet even so a tarantula has a difficult time. Prey is usually
recognized only by actual contact; a cricket half an inch
away is safe until the gap is closed.

107

The only times I have ever watched a spider closely have been in those early mornings when the orblike webs of the garden spider are beaded with dew—there is a beauty in the web if not in its maker, and there is fascination not un-tinged with horror as you watch the spider handle its first morning victim. Such spiders as these have short lives, rarely longer than a season. Eggs must be laid and left behind to carry the species through the winter. House spiders I have watched with more concern than interest. They have a tendency to fall where I want them least. These and the wolf spiders may live for five years. The tarantula beats them all, and it bothers me to think that any spider can manage to live as long as the largest whale. For it is the truth—a female tarantula and a seventy-ton blue whale may each live as long as twenty-five years. For the male taran-tulas it is another story.

Until they are sexually mature it is practically impossible to tell the sexes apart, but then sex raises its interesting and, in this case, ugly head and you begin to feel sorry for the male, more because of his inborn destiny than his immediate occupation.

The male, about eleven years old, after casting his skin for the twenty-second and last time, suddenly ceases to be a juvenile any longer and acquires his full instinctive and structural sex equipment. It is the last season of his life and he has much to do. To begin with, he makes a little web upon which he deposits drops of sperm; then he fills a special container in each of his palps by tapping the web gently at a rate of about one hundred taps per minute, for a period lasting nearly two hours—patience and determina-tion personified.

When the palps are filled, he wanders off in search of a

108

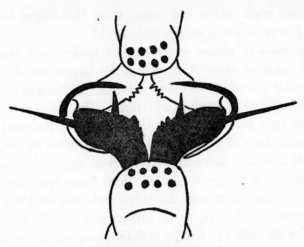

*Male tarantula (black) locking fangs
of female in his spurs.*

female, and in the mating season you can usually find a
male not far from the entrance to a female's burrow. Yet
more often than not he has to track her like a hound after a
fox, feeling and otherwise sensing the ground with his palps
and legs. When he finds her she may ignore him and may
have to be slapped to make her stir. Then, as she draws
herself angrily erect with fangs spread wide to kill, he slips
his foreleg spurs over the fangs and so secures them. He
then proceeds to mate, transferring the sperm stored within
his palps. When it is over and the next generation ensured,
he makes his cautious withdrawal and darts away, to make
a new web and repeat the venture, although only four times
at the most. Then he shrinks a little and weakens, crawls
with shaking limbs from place to place and finally stops for
good, and slowly dies—as old and senile as anyone can be.
But his mate lives on, mating and caring for her broods for
more than another dozen years, mating with eleven-year-

old males each season and eating those that linger by her side. It is a dark and savage little world.

The males of almost every kind of spider must stay on guard. In most cases the female is the larger and, if either is to make a meal of the other, it is she. And this applies to the web spiders as much as any others. The males pay court in their own peculiar way to the mistress of the web and take advantage of the silken threads. As often as not, the male is a dwarf, more expendable than ever, who tweaks the threads in a recognizable rhythm. Some spin a special thread of their own into the lady's web and by jerks and vibrations coax her on to it. Others wait on the outskirts of the web until the female is fully occupied in capturing an insect, and then run in to start stroking and tickling her into a hypnotic trance before she has a chance to bite. And still others, perhaps the most enterprising of all, catch an insect first and wrap it up as a silken package to be offered as a courting gift—anything to satisfy her hunger pains while the mating proceeds.

The spider's world is theirs and theirs alone. It seems to me no other is more alien to our own and, more than any other creature, the existence of the spider shows that we share this earth with other life and do not own it.

PART THREE

THE ROAD TO GLORY

12. out of the past

A new beginning is always difficult, whether it is the starting of an egg along the path of its development, or the study of an egg within the confines of its shell or in the dark secrecy of the womb, or the long trail that has led through time to reach hot-blooded birds and mammals, or beginning a new approach that leads to all these things.

The kingdom of animals is a community of sorts but it is made up of tribes that are kin only by the grace of their earliest beginnings. Each group has grown into its elaborate and special kind by ways that are all its own, and insects and snails and reptiles are related to one another only in so far as they are animal and have bodies made of many cells. The wonder is that they are so much alike, not that they are so different. And so, in this question of sex and reproduction and nature, we cannot build understanding of one kind upon another—and for our own beginnings in all of this we must probe along the line of backboned animals to their dim and distant past. The trail is there, murky to be sure, but out of it have come ourselves and all that means most to us in this world.

We are human beings. We are also warm-blooded mammals with all the characteristics of our class; and we and the rest are quadruped with lizards and birds and frogs, no matter what use is made of our front pair of limbs. And all quadrupeds are also vertebrates, the backboned assembly that includes all fishes and even the lamprey-eels that scourge the Great Lakes and predate fish in time and structure. Lampreys are the end of the line if we keep to creatures with some kind of backbone. When we go beyond them we land in the sea with the seasquirts. This is a long way to go, yet I believe it must be our starting point.

I bring the seasquirts into the discussion not only because I think their ancient ancestors were the kind from which our stock arose a billion years ago, but because they indicate what probably has always been the case: they are functional hermaphrodites, as we have seen. The two sexes are fully developed in every individual and eggs and sperm mature together.

The lampreys take us from the sea to the rivers, lakes and streams and to a separation into individuals that are of one sex or the other when fully mature.

In the brook lamprey, which is the one I know best, the reproductive gland develops within the body as a combination of ovary and testis—it is hermaphrodite, although not in a mature condition. For most of the lifetime of this small, eel-shaped, jawless, finless, fishy creature, even an examination of the tissue with a microscope will not tell you what its sex will be. I have gathered these lampreys by the hundred from the muddy, sandy, submerged banks of fast-flowing rivers in Quebec when the water is low enough to get down to the levels at which they live. Except for size, they all look alike, inside and out.

Only gradually, as growth continues, does one component go ahead and the other recede. Ovary and testis grow as

114

one for a long time, more or less balanced against each other in competitive effort. Then something tips the balance in favor of one or the other and, when the individual stops growing, it has either an ovary or a testis but not both. It is either a female or a male.

Yet sex means more than simply the production of eggs or sperm. There are differences in behavior even when, as in these lampreys, you cannot otherwise tell one sex from the other. For sex glands of either kind manufacture hormones, which are primarily chemical messengers although of complex and particular kinds, and liberate them into the blood stream. There they circulate and reach the brain and other organs; they make the male act like a male and the female like a female. And it seems to me almost poetic justice that lampreys, which are so slow in deciding to which sex they will belong, have difficulty in recognizing sex when they meet it.

At the place and time for mating, which is upstream in springtime, they hold on to pebbles and stones with their round, suctorial mouths. If one male holds on to the back of another male, the second male detaches himself. Both then drift downstream and separate—to swim back and try their luck again. Only when the attached individual holds fast does the male recognize his partner as a female. And only then does the mating begin. They unite in a vigorous churning of the water during which eggs and sperm are violently expelled, to mix together and be deposited. Then the more or less mutilated male and female drift with the current and soon die. They have been a means to an end —an end that has been attained.

The lateness of the swing to this sex or that in these lower vertebrates is an indecision of youth and shows how

115

evenly the balance is weighted. Even in frogs there seems to be a real struggle within the reproductive glands of each individual for one sex to dominate the other. In each frog tadpole of an early stage the rudimentary reproductive gland consists of an inner core and an outer rind. If the central core tissue grows and the rind shrinks, the frog which develops will be male; if the outer layer grows and it is the core that shrinks, the frog will be a female. Growing at the most favorable temperature, half of a crop of tadpoles swing one way and half the other to give two sexes in equal numbers. This is what the sex ratio usually is and ought to be, and the presence or absence of a sex factor in the spermatozoan usually decides which way the balance will tip. Yet it is easily overridden. When temperatures are low, the core tissue grows slower than the rind, and females predominate; at temperatures unusually high, the opposite is true and males predominate, even to ninety percent or more. The breeding season of frogs and toads must be well adjusted to the temperatures of the water in which they breed or else their sex ratio becomes lopsided.

Frogs and toads lay eggs in water, eggs that are almost as antique in kind as those of lampreys; but frogs and toads, half in and half out of water, must find each other and prepare to mate on land. Since they are among the meek and humble of this earth, they usually breed at night when the darkness makes it safer to go in search of one another. It is of course harder to find a mate at night, and the frog serenade of peeps and croaks is the answer to this problem.

When the warm spring rains arouse the frogs from their winter sleep, the odor of wet plants and the calls of frogs that have already awakened bring them together in the swamps and ponds. Like calls unto like, and carpenter

116

frogs, hop toads and pond frogs gather together in corners and do not mingle with the others—a habit which helps greatly in finding a mate. The males sing lustily from the edge of the bogs and some are dressed in colors as bright as any bird's. Little Anderson frogs of the New Jersey cranberry bogs are brilliant green with a purple front and white edgings, with golden orange under the arms and legs. Their call directs and the vision enraptures.

The male frog calls by blowing out his dewlap and letting it go with a burp—and, depending on the size, you hear the peep of a peeper or the grunt of a bull. A female may find her way to the caller from a considerable distance and may have to circle him several times or even nudge him before he stops blowing his horn and turns to embrace her. But sometimes he makes a mistake in the dark and embraces a piece of wood or another male, though with little or no

Tree frogs calling to females at night.

117

satisfaction; the wood begins to feel uncomfortable, another male croaks in protest, and the deal is off. Only when shape, size, softness, silence and acquiescence are all what they should be, and both partners feel that all is well, does the spawning proceed. Then the male grasps his mate under her armpits by means of the thickened nuptial pads on his thumbs. They grow on his thumbs only during the breeding season, only when the sex hormones flow freely in his blood. They are as distinctive of the male frog as the beard is of a man; when the male hormone secreted by the testes fails to appear in adequate amount, beards no longer grow and frogs have no thumb pads to grip with; a man's voice goes squeaky, the frog cannot croak or peep, and neither has any further interest in a female. We are all conditioned by our chemistry.

Frogs, toads, newts, and salamanders usually conduct their reproductive affairs under water, once they have managed to get together. All that their eggs have for protection against injury or shortage of water is a certain amount of albuminous jelly around them. It isn't much but it is at least a little step toward emancipation from the world of water. Because of this, some salamanders manage to lay and hatch their eggs beneath a fallen log; I have found eggs there upon occasion with the female curled around them, guarding them and helping to keep them damp with moisture from her body. Salamanders, in fact, for all their cold and clammy amphibious nature, show more likeness to the aristocratic terrestrial quadrupeds than do the high-jumping frogs; for many of them have left the water for the damp borderlands. The males of the marbled salamanders precede the females to the breeding ground in a state of tension and restlessness. You have to go out at night with flash-

118

lights into the soggy woods of early spring to see them but it is worth the effort just to see the beginnings of so much that we recognize in larger and more familiar creatures.

When the females arrive the males become even more active, performing a virtual love play in which they dash around, rubbing and butting one another and waving their tails. Then they approach the females and caress them with their snouts. Since all this happens at night in deep seclusion, looks have little meaning and odor is more important —male and female appear to smell each other out.

Eventually the male becomes sufficiently excited to discharge packages of spermatozoa shaped like miniature tree stumps, each with a broad sticky base, a whitish stalk, and a top layer containing millions of sperm. The female picks up the first package she encounters and passes it within her body, so that the eggs are fertilized before they are actually laid. And no matter how recent or how ancient a habit this may be for salamanders, I am sure that in its essentials it is a replay of the earliest steps our distant ancestors took toward bringing their eggs as well as their bodies out of the water on to the dry land.

What intermediate steps there may have been between the small aquatic egg that salamanders and frogs still lay and the large and self-contained reptilian egg that is so much like a bird's, I do not know. But the egg that is laid by a lizard, a snake, or a turtle, by all birds, and even by certain primitive hairy mammals, is one of Nature's most remarkable creations.

It is large enough and has yolk enough to develop into a small replica of its parent, and not, as with a frog, into a tadpole that is so different from the adult form. It can walk when it hatches and has no need to swim. During its

119

development it has water wrapped around it in the egg white or albumen; and around the whole there is a shell of lime that allows no water to leak out or in, but only gases like oxygen or carbon dioxide. It is a boxed-in egg with all essentials contained inside, cut off almost entirely from the outside world.

All this is fine as far as it goes. But no land vertebrate egg has a pore for sperm to enter—the sealing off is complete. Still, an egg must be fertilized. So sperm is introduced into the oviduct of the female, first because spermatozoa cannot live except in a liquid, and second because the egg must be fertilized before the shell is formed and penetration becomes impossible. Here in the first reptilian state are the basic conditions of our own reproductive process, for the mammalian egg, including the human, is derived from the older reptilian kind. In the reptile, as in man, eggs are fertilized high in the oviduct, and shells and albumen, in the case of those that have them, are added later on, as the eggs pass down the tubes. Copulation and internal fertiliza-

Male lizard displaying throat pouch to attract females.

tion are mandatory for the shelled egg of the land verte-brates, and that large and peculiar egg is perhaps their great-est invention.

Few things in the history of this planet have been so valuable as the first reptilian eggs. They were the keys to conquest, and they and their successors have been ever since—the age of dinosaurs grew out of them, the flight of birds, the uprising of the mammals and the supremacy of men. It is no wonder that a little lizard like the skink still seems to think a lot of them.

In temperate zones skinks sleep through winter, under logs or inside the loose bark of dead trees. Their blood runs cold and it takes a lot of warmth in spring to get them go-ing. The males appear in early spring, the females a little later, but both are sluggish and show no interest in each other until the sun has warmed their blood and loosened up their sinews.

When all is well, both males and females appropriate territories and defend them against outsiders, although there is some wandering back and forth, particularly by females attracted by the color and the vigorous movements of the male. Vision and color seem to dominate the senses. If you drop a male into the territory of another male, the second male goes into full display, compresses his sides so that the blue stripes stand out clear and brilliant, or else he rushes forward to attack. If the newcomer should turn out to be a dull-colored female there is no display, but the male gives a series of quick courting nods of his head and runs forward and grips her neck. As she quietens under his hold the male curls his tail under hers so that the cloacae with their genital apertures meet, and the sperm so in-troduced travels to the upper reaches of the oviducts to

121

meet the shell-less eggs. Later on, as the fertilized eggs descend in the tubes, the egg white and the protective shell are added and the eggs are laid.

Defense of breeding territory and rivalry among the males are generally found in the lizards, but other reptiles live lives that are too different to allow for it. Male snakes are attracted by the sinuous movements of the female, which is understandable, but actual recognition of sex is mainly by smell; while the sense of touch has to be well satisfied before mating can proceed. Spotted turtles of shallow brackish streams do not compete, but each female has a saffron yellow face which serves as a beacon to any male in sight—even a black and yellow stick protruding from the mud draws him to what in some way he feels must be his destiny. Without the painted face there is no mating. When the male approaches, the response of the female is to move away, though she looks back over her shoulder to make certain the lure is still working. In the painted turtle the male has elongated "finger nails" with which to stroke his partner's face. Male susceptibility, female allure, and a caress upon the cheek seem to work wonders all the way down the line.

It surprises me that sound and voice play so small a part in the life and love of reptiles, for hearing made great strides within the group; among the insects hearing and noise-making went together, although some, like moths, may hear but make no sound. Perhaps the sense of hearing among the backboned animals evolved mainly to warn of danger —and only a few, the frogs in their swamps and birds and monkeys in the tree tops, have been safe enough to raise a row on behalf of sex or society. Yet where sight, especially color vision, is well developed, silent communication is safer

122

than a noisy one and seems to be relied upon wherever possible, the more so when the searchers are fast-running lizards darting in the sun and not awkward, hopping frogs playing tag in the dark. The color of the American chameleon lizard works at a distance, and females are definitely

Pair of snakes in sexual accord.

attracted to the male with the brightest dewlap; only when they get really close do they realize that all that shines is not gold. For the dewlap seems to be no more than a signal and it takes more than a flashy front to ensure a successful mating. The inflated pouch brings a female to within a certain range—then odor becomes important and either draws the lady closer or presumably sends her darting away. She may have been curious but sexually unawakened.

Sex and reproduction go together—there is no sense to it otherwise, although sense is not everything—and in the case of reproduction it is hard to draw a line. Broodiness and attachment to one's offspring grow out of it. And usually it is the female that gets involved. She is the one that lays the eggs, most likely has to build a nest, is on the spot and, more than likely, is tired and needs to rest. Nature, being always an opportunist, takes advantage of the situation. Most reptiles provide their eggs with the necessary heat and moisture by burying them, but many do not and the blue-tailed skink is one of them. The female of this species remains with the eggs, curling herself protectingly around them. She leaves them periodically to warm herself in the sun, returning to pass on her extra body warmth to her developing eggs. The eggs are turned and moved about—the skink, in fact, will add to her clutch any eggs of her own species she may find left exposed by another female. She knows one kind of egg from another even when her eyes are covered.

Alligators and crocodiles, like catfish, live most of the time in muddy waters where visibility is low, and because

Lizard guarding her eggs.

of this perhaps they have acquired a capacity to grunt as a means of social and sexual communication. The mother alligator makes her nest out of sawgrass or other vegetation, with the eggs placed well within it. As the mass bakes in the sun it hardens so that you cannot tear it apart with your hands; nor can the young alligators get out by themselves. They cry as loud as they can and it is up to the mother lying near by to dig them out. The Nile crocodile does the same and, when the young start to call, a mother will dig under a stockade to get to them, and they stay with her usually from four to twelve months. The sounds establish the bonds between them—signals that hold parents and young together, no matter how much sight and smell may call attention to other things. It may be significant that alligators and crocodiles belong to an ancient reptilian stock more closely related to the birds than any other

125

surviving stock. What concerns us more are the bonds themselves and the influence the hormones of the body have upon them. For Nature is a builder and is forever adding to what is already present. Sex glands primarily produce eggs or sperm or both. They produce sex hormones in addition, slightly different in male and female, that bring about the distinctive colors, scent and shape of the two sexes. And they are subject to the hormones from another gland, the minute pituitary gland lying beneath the brain. The sex and pituitary hormones both come into play and between them control the time and intensity of the sexual activity, mutual relationships and, finally, maternal care. Sex is added to the sex cells and broodiness follows.

13. the chicken and the egg

To be a bird is to be alive more intensively than any other living creature, man included. Birds have hotter blood, brighter colors, stronger emotions. They are not very intelligent—they live in a world that is always in the present, mostly full of joy. It is a world unlike ours, although we too are warm-blooded vertebrates and the emotional and sexual life of a bird tells us more about our own than anything that goes on among the bees and flowers. Primarily a bird finds its living in the air—a more difficult enterprise than living on land or in the water—and most of what makes a bird the way it is relates to this. Flight and feathers and making nests in inaccessible places are part of it. Laying eggs of the kind birds do is something else, an inheritance from a reptilian past and an inconvenience, to say the least. If birds brought forth their young alive, like bats, they would be far less in jeopardy from rats and men. Flight governs their form and structure. The egg governs their life.

Most animals can fend for themselves for at least part of the time of their period of growth, but not a bird, unless it has given up all hope of flight. For until both body and wings are fully grown, to all intent and purpose, a bird does not fly; and until it flies it is dependent upon its parents for its living. Parenthood in birds is about as heavy a responsibility, it seems to me, as it is with human beings. Yet the larger the egg in proportion to the adult size of the bird, the farther along the course the chick can get before it hatches. There is every incentive to make eggs as large as possible, from this point of view. There is another. Any bird, as a flying organism, is limited in size by the lifting power of wings and muscles, and on the average the optimum size is small.

So there is a conflict, I think—the need to produce as large an egg as possible and the need to keep the egg-producer as small and light as the aerial mechanics demand. You can see what it leads to: an internal traffic jam. Two ovaries lying side by side within the abdominal cavity can function well enough as long as there is plenty of room. But when space is small and eggs are enormous—for there really is no other word for them—the system will not work. One seat is kept empty so that the oversized occupant of the other has enough room. As it happens, it is less a case of seating eggs than of finding room for oviducts. It is during the passage down the oviduct that the albumen and shell are added, and in the breeding season the oviduct with its series of eggs in transit becomes both large and heavy. Either way, space and weight between them seem to be reason enough for only a single ovary and oviduct to grow and function. How the growth of the other is held in check is something I would dearly love to know, for it

128

Ovary, tube, and shell gland of fowl.

is part of a wider problem—how a symmetrical organism can become lopsided and even reverse the pattern. The large claw of the fiddler crab, for instance, is normally on the right; but if he loses it in fighting with another male or waving too hard at a passing female, the little one on the left grows large and takes its place, while the new one which grows on the right stays small. There is a balance weighted down one way or the other, but just what the balance is

129

and what the weights consist of are bothersome questions, if you have time or concern to worry about such things.

The sexual behavior and courtship of birds is one of the most fascinating phenomena in the whole of the animal kingdom. On a somewhat more biological and less natural level, so is the nature of sex itself in birds. It is elusive to say the least.

Most of what we know comes from the common fowl. After all, we breed them and they cannot fly away. In both sexes a pair of reproductive glands are found above the kidneys where you would expect them to be. To understand what happens later you need to look at the beginnings, not merely in the chick but in the embryo near the end of the first week of incubation of the egg. To start with, the reproductive glands are more or less alike, each consisting of central cords of tissue and an outer cortical layer. But later growth makes all the difference. In the male the cortex develops no further but the central parts do and become the pair of testes; they remain in their original abdominal position close to the kidneys, and the left grows somewhat larger than the right. In the female the difference between the left and right glands becomes much greater. In the one on the right the cortical layer disappears as it does in the rudimentary testes of the male. In the left it becomes the most actively growing tissue and gives rise to the ovary. This leaves the female in a most ambiguous situation which an operation reveals. If the large, left, egg-producing ovary of a fowl is removed completely it does not grow in again, but the rudimentary gland of the right side starts to grow at once and keeps on growing. You see what happens. With the cortical layer already lost, only the central parts are there to grow, and they grow to form a testis, not an ovary, not necessarily functional it is true, although occasionally so. This brings us to the rest of it: there is far more to sex than the question which of the two components of the originally bisexual gland is going to dominate the other—and particularly so in birds.

When the left ovary is removed and the right rudiment grows to form a testis, the hen ceases to be a hen in every sense of the word. She acquires the long tail feathers and bright plumage, the large comb and wattle of the cock. In fact, what was a hen is now a cock, as masculine as can be, in behavior as well as looks. This sometimes takes place naturally—the ovary aborts by itself and the change from hen to cock occurs, though not always all the way. Change from cock to hen is much more rare though not unknown, but it can be made experimentally. A cock with its testes removed and an ovary implanted by operation loses its crow

Cock and hen of common fowl.

and comb and feathers and takes on the drab colors and submissive personality of the hen. Which introduces us to hormones. Something obviously must circulate in the blood in order to produce the effects we see.

The ovaries or testes of any vertebrate, whether of frog, hen, mouse or man, consists of more than just the reproductive cells alone: there is a connective tissue binding the other cells together. It is this that seems to be the source of the circulating agent. In terms of cells and chemistry the subject becomes complex, but what is important here is that certain chemicals, which we can call the sex hormones, are secreted into the blood stream by the reproductive glands. They are produced by cells which are not the actual reproductive cells—neither ova nor spermatozoa nor cells destined to become them. The testis produces its own particular kind of hormone, the ovary another; and on the kind and on the concentration depend the color and shape and behavior of the individual. Not that it is as simple as this—organisms never are. This is one reason why the study of living things is so fascinating and why it is so far from being an exact science. I have a feeling, and I hope it's true, that the nature of life will always in its essence elude us. When we know everything and understand it all we might as well stop—though the danger, if it is one, is remote.

Certain characteristics of behavior, color, patterns and growth depend upon the presence of one or another of the sex hormones. Yet the difference between a cock and a hen is more of a balance than anything else. Plumage, as distinct from the bird itself, is generally spoken of as cocky or henny —and this is not juvenile language—because when we look at birds as a whole we find various conditions. As a rule the cocky plumage is worn by cocks and henny plumage by the hens, yet in some the cock wears the colors of the hen and in others both the sexes may wear flamboyant cocky plumage. The common fowl again tells us much of what goes on.

When the testes of the cock are removed—a commercial practice that gives us capons—the bird remains much the same as far as feathers go. In fact, the feathers of all kinds grow longer. But the wattle and comb shrink to the size of a hen's, the crow becomes more of a cackle, and male pugnacity and courting activities virtually disappear. The bird remains beautiful, but it is masculine no longer in either the primary or secondary characteristics of the sex.

The ovaries of a hen can also be removed, although it is technically a difficult surgical operation to remove the rudimentary right one as well as the normal left. When this is done, in the brown Leghorn for instance, the bird becomes a poulard indistinguishable from a capon, except perhaps for size.

Where does this leave us? Certainly with a bird that is basically colorful, though without a sex gland of one sort or another it can neither tread a hen nor lay eggs. Injections of purified sex hormones, however, do show something of the nature of things. When the female hormone is injected into the poulard, the hen feathering gradually replaces the cocky plumage. When the injections are stopped, the bright feathers grow in again.

What does it signify? I believe it means that the real nature of a bird is to stand colorful and bright and unafraid; that birds evolved from their reptilian ancestors in security among the trees, and, having a marvelous sense of color, were able in that security to become colorful themselves; and that the colorful gaudiness at first had nothing to do with

133

sex. You see the same sort of thing among the fishes of the coral reefs. The stony jungle of the reef itself affords protection like that of trees—small fish can dart away into shelter where larger, faster fish cannot follow. And in that security color has come to life—there has been no reason to suppress it, no need to simulate invisibility as in the open sea. Away from the reefs the fish blend with the water; while on the nest a bird must be hidden or inconspicuous, blending with its surroundings in a world which now contains predatory mammals and birds of prey. Times have changed and the earth has become more dangerous for those that lay eggs and have to sit upon them. So, for the safety of the eggs and nestlings, the brooding bird acquires the drab, henny plumage and masks its natural glory, and the female sex hormone produced by the nonreproductive cells of the ovary is responsible. It also, of course, makes the hen characteristically female in her instincts and responses. In the cock the male hormone produced within the testis, although it does nothing to enhance the cocky feathering, brings about the growth of the fleshy head ornaments and the capacity to crow at dawn and at other times of triumph or command.

This is most of it, though not quite all. The sex glands, male or female, produce their sex cells and their hormones and control the general appearance and activities of the bird. As the testes and ovary grow to the active state, the secretion of their hormones also increases and the behavior of the birds toward one another changes accordingly. The gonads grow, subside, and grow again. They in turn are subject to controls—and another hormone is responsible. Here we are referred to the master gland of the vertebrate body, the small pituitary gland which lies beneath the base of the brain. One of its hormones stimulates the gonads to grow from their juvenile or their off-season reduced size to full maturity; and the sex hormones finally produced in quantity by the ovaries or testes in turn affect the pituitary gland in such a way that, so to speak, the tap is turned off. Altogether, it is a delicate, exquisite chemical mechanism for the control of the all-important timing of sexual activities and even the appearance of the animals themselves. And it is not just a case of birds, but of you and me, and frogs and fish. In fact, in almost any biological laboratory in the land in this and every spring, someone will inject a little pituitary extract into a distended female frog and find, the following morning, that she has laid all of her eggs. It works nearly every time.

In spite of all of this, I find it hard to give up the thought that sex hormones and the bright rainbow of the birds are unrelated, and as you look into the question you find that the colors are played up in sexual display, but the controls are worked in a reverse or negative sense. I believe that the true nature of the bird is indicated by its gayest colors and in the nuptial season most birds flaunt them to the utmost limits of safety. At other times a duller mantle is thrown over them and security comes first. For a bird, of whichever sex, must sit unseen upon its nest, unless it is inaccessible; and a bird must live from season to season during which danger waxes and wanes. We need to look farther than the barnyard fowl to see what happens—though not very far it is true, for we can start with ducks and drakes.

Drakes are more changeable than roosters. They molt the mating colors in the early summer and replace them with eclipse colors which are more like those of the somber female. In the fall they change back again. But a castrated drake responds to its misfortune like the rooster—it retains its brilliant mating colors indefinitely, although it is no longer a sexual bird. So it seems that the male hormone from the testis acts very much like the hormone from the female's ovary in suppressing the gaily advertising color and replacing it with camouflage. Only here it does so after the mating season is over and not all the time. The system works in a subtle way, though most effectively.

Yet even this appears to be but one way of attaining the same result. Other birds—the males of the red-billed orange weaver and indigo bunting, for instance—go through the same rhythmical molting from season to season, but they do so whether they have been castrated or not. Sex hormones play no part in the control, but injections of hormones of the pituitary kind bring about the change to henny plumage. It looks as though the pituitary has taken over direct control.

To reproduce successfully, a bird needs not only to be in the right place at the right time, but, almost more than any other creature, to be in the right state at the right time. This means that male and female must synchronize their activities and emotions to a remarkable degree.

The trouble now, I find, is to choose among the multitude of birds those which seem more interesting or outstanding than the rest. Each kind deserves a place—but that would mean a bird book and this is something else. Neither do I think we should lump them all together and say birds do this and birds do that—it is a tendency we have, but it takes the living out of life, and I, at any rate, cannot think of a gannet and a wren together without losing something vital

136

out of each. Certain seabirds, for instance, are better studied than birds in general, although it is merely a question of taste which kind of bird best serves our purpose.

When the laughing gulls come north to the islands off Cape Cod in springtime, thousands upon thousands of them, they settle at first in loose flocks of a much smaller size which become local nesting communities. At first the days

Male heron handing over nest material to female
in act of ceremony.

137

are spent in feeding, flying, visiting and squabbling. Then, one of the birds within a group discovers its voice has changed, and a loud clear call replaces its winter squeak. Either male or female may give the signal, and then the rest join in. The call in any case is a call for action, and any virile males within twenty feet or so arouse themselves and charge the calling bird. If the singer should be a male itself it usually retreats, but a female more or less holds her ground in the face of the challenge, drawing herself up stiffly and flagging her head. Sex is a question of behavior in such birds as these, and finding a partner is difficult and complicated. It would be simple enough if only two birds were involved, but birds are social creatures and it rarely happens that way; and when laughing gulls get together and the sap begins to flow it is rather like a game. In a small group the first problem of a lusty male, after running at a female and recognizing her by her standing firm, is to get rid of any near-by competitors. So, one at a time, he charges them as well, and those that are males retreat and fly away. This leaves him, as a rule, with more than one female, too much for his monogamous personality. One female, therefore, drives the rest away and only the pair are left. And in so far as the vigor of their drives is an indication of their readiness to mate, the surviving pair are obviously well attuned to one another. The courtship can proceed.

More and more, the two indulge in a mutual courtship feeding of a purely symbolic kind, while the male issues long, plaintive sex moans. When at last they seem to be so well acquainted that they can distinguish each other from all of their neighbors, they go off on their own. The male goes first to select the site and then calls the female to him. When she lands beside her moaning mate she begs frenziedly for food. The food ceremonial becomes more and more real; the lady gets fish although she has to beg for it—the ritual is important for it seems to lead directly to the positions assumed in actual mating, an action that demands complete cooperation since fertilization must be internal although there are no external organs to ensure its process. After mating, both birds share in building the nest, the male collecting, the female constructing; later on, they take turns in brooding the eggs. All of it is necessary. There are no short cuts in the psychological, physiological, reproductive sequence.

Such is the pattern rather generally found among sea birds. It is as hard for a bird to distinguish another from the rest of its kind as it would be for you or me. A penguin goes around offering a pebble or a feather to all and sundry and can only tell a lady from a gentleman by the reception he gets. The selection of a responsive partner, the mental imprinting of means of identification, and the mutual building up to a synchronized climax all seem to be essential to a successful mating. And even when the actual mating is past and eggs are there to be sat upon, the mutual courtesies and ceremonies continue. This is particularly the case when the plumage of the two sexes is alike, such as in the great crested grebe, the red-throated diver, the gannet and the albatrosses. Billing and bowing are the rule—beaks clashing and clattering together as though they were fencing, or the two birds standing apart and waving their wings and bowing in measure like folk dancers. Why do they do it? The emotional bond between a pair is apparent enough, yet this is something that goes beyond sex in its limited sense. In some way the ceremonials seem to bring satisfaction and a sense of well-being to the individual and perhaps

139

prosperity to the race. There is a building-up and main-tenance of tension which brings interest and loveliness into life.

Yet whatever the lasting psychological values of the emotional attachment and responsiveness may be, it does have biological value: it holds the pair together long after actual mating is over—for a few weeks in sparrows, for life in geese—and transforms the mated couple into a pair of parents with a mutual interest in incubating eggs and feeding nestlings. The stronger the ties that unite them, the greater the security of the reproductive unit of parents and offspring—the family, in fact. It works in birds as well as men.

14. dance, wings

and song

Birds, most of them, are social creatures. The solitary bird is like the solitary man: each is out looking for something connected with earning its living, we hope. When the search for food is not uppermost there is a tendency to get together and take notice of one another. Perhaps having two legs in place of the old-fashioned four, and having vision as the dominant sense instead of smell, does something to the system. I do not know. Perhaps a sense of rhythmic motion comes from the skill in balancing on two points instead of four and from a gaze no longer governed by a nose. The fact remains that only men and birds are bipeds—and only birds and men can really dance. Men includes women, too, but I do not feel that the supplicating spider male should be in this particular party, although the fireflies seem to belong. And I am uncertain how much of this concerns sex, although the one certainly becomes involved with the other.

It seems to begin with sexual rivalry and the infectious

nature of the activities that go with displaying and courting. Black guillemots that take the place of penguins in northern seas, well tailored in black and white during the breeding season, are incessantly active whether they swim or dive in choppy waters among the bays, or bill and sigh in high-pitched wheezings on the rocks. Couples may drift or swim about in a seemingly casual way, and then suddenly you realize they have arranged themselves in a long line with the individual birds evenly spaced. Or several couples in a social party all at once plunge and swim in the cold green depths like glassy butterflies. Competition may have started things but the outcome is co-operative enjoyment instead of struggle. If a southern penguin takes up an ecstatic attitude and begins to call, hundreds of others join in at once, while any jay will stop whatever it may be doing to join in any screaming party that is going on. In a yelling crowd a man may yell and not know what he yells for. Yet birds and men can be truly themselves only within their societies, and out of their communal nature comes the dance and other social graces.

The oldest communal dancing that we have ourselves is the ring type—but turkeys do it too, in a follow-my-leader-round-a-tree style. Moreover, the male of the rose-colored starling, in crouching posture, does a circling dance around the female, with short quick steps and vibrating quills, singing all the while. The lady at first is passive but soon is drawn to join him and round they go, faster and faster; then suddenly they mate. The mating dance of the Goonies —an albatross—is more majestic. Male and female stand face to face with wings partly spread, surrounded by a large circle of shouting and clacking onlookers. The two per-formers raise their heads toward the sky, then duck to the

142

ground only to rise again touching beak to beak. The beaks are ducked first under the left wing and then the right, and heads are reared once more to the sky—dancers match- ing step for step. As the rhythm increases the clacking of the outer circle reaches a crescendo—and if the dancing male should tire or falter, another waiting on the sidelines slips in and takes up the dance. The ceremony broadens and is no longer a purely private party.

Birds are like men, emotionally and in their sense of rhythm, but they have little power of reason; their dances demand only a minimum of memory and anticipation. The limit, I think, is seen among the razor bills that have a paddling dance on the surface of the sea. At first they move in single file, then converge toward each other until their raised beaks almost touch in the center of the group—it is even more uncanny since the moving feet are invisible be- neath the water. The circle swells, then breaks—each pair of birds bob, come together and hold beaks, and for a few seconds waltz around each other. Then a single file once more, with beaks and tails lifted as high as possible, and then again the ring, the ecstatic facing of the pairs, the waltzing, and back to the file in the state of rapture. It is as good a description of a folk dance as any I have heard of. And what is sex to start with ends up, it seems, as pure enjoyment of rhythmic patterns of motion.

Birds dance and so do we—and so do apes, particularly the chimpanzee. In one account, which is typical, two of them in mock fighting dragged each other about the ground until they came to a post, which they began to circle. One by one, the rest of the group appeared and joined the circle, marching behind each other around the post in an orderly way. The pace grew faster and the walk became

143

a trot, stamping with one foot and putting the other lightly down to beat out a rhythm and keep in step. Sometimes heads bobbed up and down with mouth hanging loosely open, all in rhythm and all in obvious enjoyment of the dance. And wherever possible, strings and vines bedecked the body, to swing and dangle as they moved about. It is, of course, a social dance entirely and has nothing to do with sex, although chimpanzees often perform a dance of a sort before they mate, consisting of a rhythmic pounding of the ground with feet or hands or both, or clapping the hands together, building up the tension and excitement. One male performed a dance in triple rhythm in front of several females. We do not stand so quite alone in this world as we are generally led to think.

Dancing and display are mixed up together in the conduct of most kinds of birds, and concern the acquiring and stimulating of a mate—the dance for the sake of the dance alone, without dishonorable intentions, is one of the rarer distillates. We ought to know.

It would be difficult to overestimate the power that sight and sound exert on the mind and actions of a bird. Even humans have a better sense of smell and an infinitely greater sense of touch. When eggs are laid which are precious as birds' eggs usually are, when nestlings are as hard to raise as they seem to be, parental community of endeavor makes all the difference to the chances for success. "Two minds with but a single thought, two hearts that beat as one" requires continual and nurturing attention, whether human or avian. Common efforts and mutual rites smooth the way to conjugal accord. For a bird, rhythmic movement, perhaps with sound as well, most readily achieves and expresses the unified measure of emotion. More often, the ritual of select-

144

ing a mate not only paves the way to actual mating but sets a seal upon it. When a gander has driven off a rival and has been accepted by a goose, they both utter a clarion cry. It is the shout of triumphant union which consummates the pair-formation, not the subsequent act of copulation—and in this case the pairing is for better or for worse until death do them part.

Displaying before a female, whether it takes the form of a dance or a strutting in a garment of brightly colored feathers, or fighting for supremacy with other males, demands a stage. What the stage is called depends on whether it is used for group activities or whether it serves for display by an individual bird. The first is an arena, the other a court, and the terms themselves take us some way into the world of the birds.

In the case of the ruff and the prairie chicken the arena serves as a mating station—it is sex pure and simple, and promiscuity rules the roost; the mated reeve and female chicken have no further interest in the male after mating is accomplished. For the rest of the time, the two sexes might be separate species going their independent ways.

As winter gives way to spring, the cocks of the prairie chicken begin to gather twice a day on their arena or booming grounds, starting before sunrise. At first, there may be general fighting over the whole of the arena, but gradually each cock establishes a territory or court of his own where he displays and performs such acts of mating as opportunity affords. He struts and inflates his air sacs, letting them out with a resonant boom. The females arrive later, usually late in March; when one of them approaches the arena, there is an outburst of booms and excited dancing. The early hens get rushed, but in early April when

145

Hen's view of Prairie Chicken.

hens are visiting the grounds in numbers the procedures are more orderly. The females assemble in loose flocks, move around in a leisurely way and mate as a rule with any cock whose court they enter upon. Later on, when the peak of visiting has passed and hens become scarce, the sanctity of a court is disregarded and a cock and a hen get interference from the other cocks.

The reason for all of this may be a superfluity of males. Whatever the sex ratio of the prairie chicken at the time of hatching, when we come to the breeding birds themselves the males appear to outnumber females by about two to one. The regular pairing and long-term attachments acquired by other birds may become impossible when the

146

one to one ratio is upset for any cause—too much masculine competition and too little privacy mitigate against even a semipermanent partnership, as Hollywood seems to show. Whatever it is, the self-sufficient hens are assured that their eggs will be fertilized—there are not only more than enough eagerly awaiting males, but their period of sexual readiness begins sooner and lasts longer than the females', so that hens are satisfied, eggs are all fertilized, and only the cocks with their fine feathers and calls are left not knowing exactly what to do. There seem to be so many ways in which a male can become ridiculous.

The same booming ground of prairie chicken may be used year after year, even though a road may be built across it, and some arenas go back beyond the tribal memory of local Indians. Yet there always has been plenty of space and the vigorous but not too serious fighting among the males may in part reflect this freedom. In the ruff it is somewhat different.

Ruffs arrive in Europe from their winter quarters in Africa and Asia to their customary places during spring, arriving in the early morning hours until possibly twenty are gathered together in one arena, each with his tiny court staked out. No two birds are alike; one has a purple ruff, another a white one, another a black or maybe ginger. Like the prairie chicken, the ruffs fight among themselves, though with even less serious intent and mainly to set the limits of their courts. Between periods of territorial bickering they are peaceful enough and display to each other, even though all are males. The display is peculiar and consists of three phases: the bird at first rushes wildly in all directions with ruff erect; then he suddenly comes to a halt; finally, with wings half open and the ruff held out

147

erect, the bird sinks slowly down, with head bowed, until its beak sticks in the ground, oblivious to all about it and quivering in obvious ecstasy. At last, it rises gently, preens itself, takes a short flight or goes to sleep. Such is the behavior of the male when left all to itself.

When a reeve arrives, the ruffs all stand up and flap their wings in ritual greeting. They rush and threaten one another for awhile with no harm done; then they go into an extreme portrayal of their ecstatic attitude. All stand still while the sober little female calmly walks around and looks them over. The male with the best-looking ruff is likely to be chosen and she indicates her choice by touching his head or fondling his feathers—then they go off together and the other ruffs take her decision in the only way gentlemen in high stiff collars can. It may, of course, be a question of room once again, with arena space restricted and individual courts reduced to little more than small, circular depressions worn by the feet of the ruff. Good manners

Ruffs posturing before a visiting Reeve.

148

come from living in crowded quarters where give and take is essential and, should you care for analogies, ruffs and reeves belong to the Old South while prairie chickens are prairie folk. The ruff holds his place and expresses his ardor in perfect silence; the prairie chicken booms across the open spaces.

It is one thing to hold court in an open arena and quite another to do so in the Panamanian jungle. Yet, this is the setting for the little black and yellow manakins.

The cock manakin makes an elliptical court, some thirty by twenty inches across, on the forest floor by clearing away every leaf and twig until the earth is as bare as if swept by a broom. Neighboring courts are usually about thirty feet apart, set out in a line roughly parallel to the shore of a lake or stream. The manakin frequents his court and its surroundings during the daylight hours of the breeding season, flying away to feed every two or three hours but never staying away for long.

Females are leaf green in color and difficult to see, though not for manakin males. As soon as one comes into view each cock within range flits from branch to branch whirring and calling until he nears his court. He enters it with a loud snap made by his wings that can be heard for three hundred yards—and with a snap-snap springs from one side of the court to the other. It is all done by the dancing, snapping invitation—the female has her choice and, if she chooses to accept, she joins in and the two birds leap rhythmically across the court, passing in midair. When the duet comes to an end the couple disappear into the more secluded privacy of the forest.

Manakins are sexually active for four to eight months out of the year, but whatever the sexual condition of the

149

female may be she apparently has to be courted before she will receive a male. And courting must be conducted in the proper place. When male manakins leave their courts to pursue the females in the tree tops the result is confusing and unsatisfactory to all. Yet, what the value of the system really is I do not know. An unbalanced sex ratio perhaps comes into the picture; it may be mainly a device for arranging partners and synchronizing their emotional and sexual state; and it may, at least in part, be a case of selecting the mate with the greatest virility—the male with the brightest colors and the most active display is chosen, and racial vigor is enhanced. Certainly, the court and arena system stimulates both sexes. In an experiment with a stuffed and mounted female manakin, a male copulated with it eighty-five times within an hour. This also shows that for a sexually excited bird, at least, looks are completely deceiving.

Manakins, like ruffs and prairie chickens, have no regular mates. The females only visit the males to pair, after which each retires in solitude to build her nest and raise her brood alone. It leaves the males with time to play. Gould's manakin is the one that holds the courts that we have seen, but there are many other kinds, and twice a traveler from Brazil has told of a group of manakin males that sat around in a circle, hopping up and down in beat with the rhythm of a song that another manakin was piping just outside the group. This may be, however, just a traveler's tale twice told.

It seems clear enough that where there is a regional or actual surplus of males, Nature finds it more effective for

the birds to compete for a female by displaying from a private court where trespassing is not thought of, rather than
to stage a free-for-all rush upon the lady. It reduces fights
among the males and more of them live to mate another day.
More important the system facilitates the process of mating
without harm to either sex, while ensuring that the male in

Golden Pheasant displaying before female.

151

the best form and condition is the one to effect it. It puts a premium on the health and vigor of the male as a propagating organism and not on the male who happens to see her first.

A court in this sense becomes the center of a territory, and breeding territories are claimed by many birds who have no court more recognizable than a certain tree or an unmarked area of ground. When a cock displays within its territory, it not merely advertises its charms to a possibly observant female but in effect warns other males not to come too close. The latent threat of a fight is there, but as a rule the warning is respected. It is not a question of intelligence—birds, most of them, have become psychologically so conditioned through inheritance that an individual becomes a coward governed by fear as he approaches the heart of another's territory, but rages with anger if another encroaches upon his own. When fear and anger meet, anger wins and often wins without a fight.

Territorial rights are generally respected and, if only for this reason, it becomes important for a male to find and stake his claim while claims are still to be found. At close quarters, bright feathers or curious postures may give each contestant a small space to itself, as courts within an arena, but when birds are small and the breeding territory for each is large, sight alone does not suffice and sound is called into play in the form of song. When the robin arrives with the spring and sings from the top of a tree, he stakes his claim. No other robin will sing within a certain distance of the source of that outpouring of melody—the claim is filed as definitely as if it were at a land office where a new region was being opened for settlement. And for a time it is a matter exclusively between males—robins sing and territories are established before the females arrive from the south. Only after their arrival does the spring song become a call for a mate as well as a keep-off sign.

Yet it would be a mistake to speak simply of a bird whistling for its mate, or dancing, or displaying colors, or flying slowly to and fro like a giant pendulum, which is what one hummingbird does. A bird is neither human nor intelligent, but for all of that a bird, any bird, is complex. When it comes to wooing, all the possible stops are pulled within certain limits of safety. I know this metaphor is mixed,— but so is the subject. Thus it is a rare bird that does not combine some distinctiveness of song and flight, color and posture, in order to establish itself in the mind of a prospective mate or to emphasize his presence to another male. The greenshank even ascends to a height of two thousand feet in rapid flight and then rises and falls in aerial acrobatics, all the while uttering his passionate love song.

Crested screamers of the Argentine ascend in a musical soaring flight in pairs—they are said to mate for life and their duet accentuates the harmony of their respective rhythms. The male begins, the female takes up her part, and together they pour out a torrent of sound, some deep like drumbeats, others clear and ringing—the loudest sound in the silent pampas. In the Central American rain-forest, as night descends and the howler monkeys send their thundering roaring concert throughout the jungle, wood quail stand face to face, male and female, and sing in harmony and rhythm so perfect that it seems to be a single song.

Song alone can be more distinctive, more penetrating, and more controlled than any dance or colored patterns. All music affirms this; the melody and quality of sound that birds make have variety without end. The song is language

153

of a kind—if only birds had more mind and less emotion they might show their paces better. As it is, the song is used for any of a dozen purposes: to identify its owner to its kind, to show where the bird and its territorial limits lie, its vigor and dominance, its sexual state, its nest site; or to make another bird disclose its sex, to drive off a male or attract a female, to bring a pair of birds into sexual harmony, or to call a mate from the nest. It is signaling by means of sound, packed with meaning except when sheer excess of energy demands an outlet—the fact that what is primarily and essentially utilitarian so often turns out to have lyric beauty is something to think about. I believe beauty is inherent in the nature of our universe and shows itself where it can— it is not only in the mind of the human beholder.

There are few birds more unlovely than an old crow. This does not mean that a crow sees less of color and movement around it than do other birds—in fact, the perception of a solitary crow perched sentinel-like on the top of a dead tree is notorious. Yet crows are neither beautiful nor do they sing. Large birds seem to have more trouble with their voices than small ones do, and some kinds are in any case less well equipped for song than others. It is a question of anatomy—like the change in his Adam's apple which transforms the boy soprano into the unmelodious singer that most men become. Only in the case of birds such differences in size and shape affect a singing box which lies at the bottom of the windpipe, not at the top like our own. A crow caws in a raucous manner that pleases no one except a crow, and its relatives are not much better—jays, scream, magpies chatter, and the raven croaks, sounds as discordant as the air can carry.

Yet I know from personal experience that you can appreciate music and art without being able to reproduce it yourself, and while I feel there is a vast difference between the emotional spirit of a warbler and that of a crow, I suspect that I am wrong and that a crow is no less a bird for all its hoarse voice and drab exterior. A magpie in its white and black raiment is as handsome as they come, but it still is a kind of a crow. If jays were only as melodious as their colors are bright, we would rank them as high as any—yet their kinship with the crow is a close one.

What I am leading up to is this: the crow family is afflicted by a throaty voice of little use for singing and can make little use of song. However, when it comes to color, certain of their relatives are remarkable. For example, the birds of paradise live up to their name—for beauty of color and form, and for its display, they belong to a world of their own. Yet, while they are not placed with the crows themselves, their family is related to them and contains members that are just as unattractive. Bower birds also are related and are not spectacular in themselves; yet they show an appreciation of color that is unsurpassed. And it is not just a case of pretty feathers or a liking for brightly colored objects, although these are present—it is a vital part of sex and reproduction.

Birds of paradise are many and must be seen, photographically or in reality, to be appreciated—most zoological gardens possess some, which is fortunate since New Guinea, which they inhabit, is so far away and out of reach.

When bird of paradise skins were first imported into Europe, four or five centuries ago, a host of legends grew up

155

about them. They arrived with feet and legs cut off, which added to the wonder, and were thought to be birds from Paradise in very truth. Such birds as these were thought to live their lives high in heaven, never coming down to earth except by accident, and so without need of feet. They lived on the dew of heaven and the female laid her eggs on the back of the male where they were warmed by the heat of the sun. Fantasy to be sure, though closer to the truth than you would think, for all belong to the tropical rain forests and for the most part live in the tops of the highest trees. For all of that, they were almost exterminated by trappers before protective laws were passed to save them.

The roof tops of a rain forest teem with brilliant and fantastic life, but it is as much out of reach as the great ice barrier of Antarctica where in dark mid-winter the emperor penguins lay their eggs and hatch their young. Birds of paradise and emperor penguins are better known in captivity than they are at home, so naturally what we know is not enough. Yet one of them at least—the great bird of paradise—gathers early in the morning in small bands upon a particular tree and goes through a dance which displays its plumes, accompanied by much loud calling. The males gather together, I should say, for the females are dull brown and gray birds of a most inconspicuous kind. The male in this case is chestnut brown with magnificent yellow plumes springing from each side and trailing beyond the tail. The bird signals the beginning of display with a loud "wak-wak-wak" that can be heard through the forest for a mile. Then, to the accompaniment of a low croaking call, the dance commences—wings open, plumes are raised, the state of ecstasy becomes intense; then wings droop and plumes rise above the back, falling in a cascade. The whole bird is

156

overshadowed by then, with crouching body, yellow head and emerald green throat forming the pedestal for the golden glory waving above from a deep red base. A loud call, a shaking of the plumes, and the display is over.

Each kind of paradise bird has its own kind of feathery brilliance and displays it to the best effect. The dance is fitted to the raiment and, in some at least, the calling has become melodious. Many of the paradise birds assemble together in trees to display at dawn and mating is probably promiscuous. The six-wired bird of paradise hops like the manakin from bough to the ground and back, while the magnificent bird of paradise goes all the way down and clears a court, even tearing away leaves from shrubs to allow the light to shine upon him. There is mystery here—too little is known; is the court in this case something new or a carry-over from the past? I think perhaps it is new, for New Guinea forests are safer for birds than those of the Asiatic mainland; the more efficient carnivora have not reached it and it is reasonably safe for a large, spectacular bird to display on the ground instead of in a tree—and for a large bird the act of mating may be easier on the ground. But the display needs to be brighter the darker the stage becomes, and you can argue this question either way: birds of paradise acquired their plumes and piercing calls for impressing females in the semidark and only later took their colors to the tree tops in the sun. It is always interesting to speculate on such things as this, when you have half the facts you need and can dream up the rest in possibly half a dozen different ways. There is more life in thinking than in knowing.

Until man entered the picture and brought some other creatures with him, New Guinea and Australia, and some other islands, had been a sanctuary for many kinds of birds and primitive mammals. How safe these places are is shown by the brush turkey of New Guinea, which lays her eggs and covers them with a pile of vegetation, leaving them to incubate and hatch as best they can without further help from her.

The point is this—display of sexual decoration before a female can be carried to a greater length both in intensity and in time when danger from lurking mammals is virtually nonexistent. And, until recently, this has been the case. The lyre bird of Australia proves it, I believe—a bird in many ways like the birds of paradise, though not related to them, but better known to man—and suffering from that acquaintance.

Lyre birds live in the depths of the ancient tree fern and gum forests. I put it in the present because I hope it still is true, although the appearance of the lyre bird on Australian postage stamps is an ominous sign. You need to think of the bird as bird of paradise, manakin, ruff, mockingbird and half a dozen others all rolled into one.

The bird is large, about the size of guinea fowl, though with graceful head and neck, and long powerful legs. The body of the male is a dark blue-brown; the tail, with its iridescent lyre-shaped plumes and the fan between, is a wonder to behold. The female, as usual, is much less impressive.

About the end of April—which is not the spring season in the southern hemisphere—the males build courts. In fact, each male builds several courts in an extensive and well-defined territory of his own. Old courts are built up as well as new, and one bird, at least, had twenty. Each court is a mound upon which the male can display his plumage with-

158

out getting all mixed up with adjacent ferns, and from each mound in turn he sings his songs—possibly the largest and most lovely repertoire on this earth—which can be heard clearly several hundred yards away.

It is the old court system with a difference—almost as though there is an arena but only a solitary male to make it, keeping up a pretense of competition among a group of males by making a number of mounds and singing in turn from each point of display. The mating season—if we can call it that, for this, too, is strange—begins in May and the female watches the dance and listens to the song of the neighboring male each time he performs. When a performance comes to an end, both birds go off in search of food, but as soon as the male begins again the lady leaps on to a branch the better to see. Throughout May and June all the male's power of mimicking other birds' songs is called into play, but from then until mid-July the song changes into the long, warbling, mellow, nuptial song of his own kind—singing it over and over from dawn until dark. During this period the birds are never apart, going from mound to mound, at each of which the male stops to sing and display his manly charms. Then the mating occurs and the hen stays home to sit on her egg—the male goes back to mimicking other birds and soon begins to molt. It takes four years to reach maturity, and pairing is said to be for life; only one chick a year is produced.

What has happened? There is clearly a restriction in numbers and I know of no evidence that there is any surplus of males. And note the seasons! Courting begins in early May, which is the start of the southern winter, and ends in mid-July. The chick hatches from the egg late in August, which is the end of such winter as there is.

The answer to all of this comes from the study of the bowerbird, the last one on our list. It also is an Australian, although found in New Guinea, too, and while it is kin to birds of paradise it is unadorned. Yet both the male and female have an eye for color. And this time we know something of the inner workings of the bird, in addition to its outward behavior.

The unique feature of most bowerbirds is that during the breeding season the males build small ceremonial houses set neatly in clearings and furnished with a variety of objects used in display and carefully piled up in a cleared area in front of the bower when not in use. The bower is not a nest and is made by the male alone—for all its complexity it is a court, and the nest itself is made at another time by the female without help from the male.

The bower of most true bowerbirds is a simple double-walled construction on the ground, with an outer part of thin twigs and an inner of grass stems, altogether about six inches thick, two feet long and a foot and a half high. In Central Queensland forests the bowers of the spotted bowerbird are usually built along the path of the sun—although the satin bowerbird always orientates its bower across the sun's path in a north-south direction. Unless we get into regions of mystic powers and interpretations, it seems to me that it is a question of illumination and time of display. Where trees are not too thick, an east-west direction allows the sun to shine into the bower at dawn and dusk. Where only the midday sun succeeds in reaching down to the forest floor, a north-south orientation alone would allow its rays to enter the entrance of the bower.

Each kind of bowerbird builds its own particular kind of bower—they vary a lot and so do the decorating habits of the builder. I believe all are collectors, but the spotted bowerbird has a fondness for bleached bones and egg shells, crab shells and pebbles, anything that reflects light, together with berries and cones and seedpods—and now that so-called civilization has come within reach you may find glass, nails, knives, spoons, thimbles and coins, almost anything small and bright, added to the pile. The satin bowerbird chooses chiefly blue and yellow decorations. While the tooth-billed bowerbird has a saw tooth and cuts off leaves which it turns sunny side up to catch the light. And many of the birds go even further and paint the walls of their bowers with fruit pulp or with dry grass chewed up with saliva—anything to make the bower as bright as possible, compensating for the darkness of the woods and the lack of vivid color in the bird itself. No matter what, it seems, the eye and the interest of the female must be caught and held.

Male and female associate as a pair in July when the birds leave the autumnal feeding flocks and bower building begins, and while the male calls the female to the bower and goes in search of her if she strays away, it is not pair formation in the sense we find it in other birds, but a maintenance of day-to-day interest in each other during a long premating period. The male displays at his court—I see no other way to put it—and the essence of display is sudden movement, noise and sudden erection of any colored feathers the bird possesses, picking up and tossing objects from his collection. The female looks on with a quiet intensity. If she goes away, the male turns to housekeeping for a while, quietly rearranging his decorations and even eating some of the ornamental berries.

Intermittent display is kept up for several or even many months, until the female accepts the male with the onset of

161

early summer. Then she goes off, like the lyre bird, to build her nest and hatch her young, while the male goes on displaying at the bower—a grass widower, perhaps, but not exactly unattached. For when the young are fledged, the female brings them to the bower for a week or two and the whole family engages in communal display activities. And like the lyre birds once again, though the birds are not related, it takes four or five years for the young to reach maturity, an astonishing length of time for any bird.

Bower building commences when the testes of the male show their first sign of seasonal growth, usually in late July or August. Ovulation in the female occurs in November or December. The young hatch out even later at the beginning of the monsoon period when insect life is most abundant. And this seems to be our answer. It applies to the lyre bird as well as the bower. The males commence to build mounds or bowers when their testes start to grow and the seasonal flow of sex hormones begins—castration puts a stop to it. From the male point of view—not a conscious one—the sooner this happens the better perhaps, because breeding territories are limited and established ones respected, and competition is keen. If you are young and want to find a place, you cannot be a laggard. However this may be, the female is in a different situation altogether. She can mate when she is ready—there are males enough and more. Her concern—racially speaking—is to lay her eggs at the time best suited to the feeding of her chicks when they hatch. She waits for spring to mate. So you see where it leaves the male. He is ready months before a female quickens, yet all he can do is to gain and hold her interest with antics and noises and by dangling pretty things before her eyes—it is either that or have some other male supplant him. It is not

162

a matter of intelligence, for once his sex hormones begin to excite him he cannot help but start his construction and display. Yet for about two or three months he has to keep his lady in his pasture and keep his own sexual intensity high, for in birds as well as man, psychological and esthetic aspects enter into sex, as well as hormones. What finally brings the female into readiness to mate comes probably from the environment itself—a seasonal change detectable in the depths of the dark rain forest that promises the coming of the season of insect plenitude. The long period of masculine attendance upon an unawakened mistress probably has led to the elaboration of the ceremonies he finds necessary to hold her. If nothing more, building a bower and keeping house gives him something to while away his time—leisure is necessary for the arts and crafts; and the lyre bird makes music, though his lyre is mute.

15. the night of our forebeing

We may envy the birds their powers of flight and song, which many of them obviously enjoy; and there is something to be said for living in the present to the extent that birds do, with little memory of the past and no real anticipation of what is yet to come—intensely conscious of sight and sound, strongly swayed by joy and anger, and sometimes petrified by ecstasy or fear. We share a past in common with them, have the same general ground plan in our bodies, have the same glands for producing reproductive cells and sexual hormones. Yet, from some ancient reptilian stocks the birds went one way and mammals went another, and we look across to the avian world as though across a chasm. Birds and mammals have lived alongside in time through a hundred million years—but in worlds of different dimensions. To find our own beginning, we need to retrace our steps.

We are mammals, and so are a mouse and a kangaroo. We all have hair and warm blood and suckle our young—

speaking for species and not for sex. But two creatures that qualify on these grounds, the platypus and the spiny ant-eater or echidna, which are admitted to our class, fail to conform in at least one important way—they do not bring forth their young alive but lay eggs in almost, but not quite, the old reptilian manner. They are relics, to be sure, safely isolated until recent times in Australasia, and surviving through the ages as the result of certain peculiarities of habit and structure: they are adept at getting and staying out of sight—the platypus in burrows or in the water, the other by digging. Both are specialists in hideaways.

The early history of mammals as a race apart, and there-fore of you and me, is shrouded in darkness. This of course is a metaphor, but it may be almost literally true as well. The trend toward mammalian rank started, according to the fossil record, surprisingly long ago when the reptiles them-selves had barely found their place. Mammal-like reptiles lived long before the age of the great dinosaurs, and crea-tures that we might well have recognized as less specialized relatives of the platypus and echidna evolved from reptiles

Platypus (left) and Echidna (right), the only two surviving egg-laying mammals.

165

at about the time the coniferous forests and the more fantastic reptilian monsters were coming into being. And then we lose the trail.

Mammalian fossils turn up in numbers only after the age of reptiles has come and gone—yet in spite of the fact that we cannot find their fossil bones the evolving mammals must have been there all the time. What does it mean? I think you find the answer in the echidna and the platypus. The primitive mammals were there throughout the age of reptiles, but they lived in an age of terror, and were not too numerous or too large and kept well out of sight. In an age of greater power they had to live circumspectly or not at all; they developed wits instead of brawn and paid more attention to their eggs and young. And there was time—time beyond all imagining—in which these oppressed but surviving remnants of the original crop of mammal-like reptiles could perfect their equipment for living and reproducing. When the ruling reptiles finally disappeared, for reasons still difficult to understand, the mammal was ready to exploit the earth. We still are doing it, but the making of the mammal—all our essentials of reproduction that distinguish us from reptiles—took place while the evolving mammal was in hiding, foraging probably only by night and serving time as the meek and humble for more than a hundred million years before the earth could be inherited. It was time enough for anything to happen, and most of it did.

We can reckon the process of change as three phases or steps of departure from the original reptilian state. The first led to the egg-laying mammals, although not so peculiar as our platypus and echidna which are modern descendants fitted to special ways of living. The second established the marsupials, such as the opossum and kangaroo, with emphasis upon a pouch for carrying helpless young. And the last brought forth the placentals to which men, mice and elephants now equally belong. All this is reproduction and much of it concerns sex, but there is a twisted thread in the story that intrigues me a lot. It is a question of color.

We are inclined to take the world around us for granted and believe what we see. Yet some of us are color blind and what we see is not the same to all. Bees and other insects have color vision—both flowers and experiments seem to prove it. But who else has it? It is not at all easy to discover, yet I think there is little doubt that most fishes see color and so do most of the reptiles, although snakes seem to be without it. It is a sense that belongs to the light of day, and the birds have kept and developed all that the reptiles ever had. They see color and make use of it. The mammals for the most part do not.

The birds grew out of reptiles and kept their sense of color. The mammals grew out of reptiles and grew color blind. It clinches the suspicion that during their long eclipse throughout the age of dinosaurs, an eclipse that lasted for close upon eternity, they hid in darkness by day and searched for food by night—color had no meaning and eyes became adapted to seeing among the shifting shadows of the dusk and dark; the color cones of the retina disappeared. This, of course, is speculative: you cannot judge the color sense of any fossil, let alone a fossil you do not find. Yet the fact is this: that horses and cattle, dogs and cats, raccoons, mink, rats, mice and rabbits are all color blind—and it seems most likely that color blindness is general among all but one of the mammalian groups.

When you think of it, mammals as a whole are a drab lot.

167

They go in for patterns of black, brown, yellow and white—all of them blending or camouflaging shades and patterns, all painted with a brush that exploits the range of a single. yellowish pigment between the extremes of white and a brown so deep it appears to be black. There is no color—no bright greens or reds or blues to serve in display whether as warnings or as sex appeal. The whole group of placental mammals has been dragged through some ancestral colorless knothole. This is a pity, for a rainbow-colored elephant would be even more salutary than a pink one.

To all of this there is an exception. We see color—obviously—and make much of it; we delight in it and it in turn colors our emotions. We wear color—as paint and uniforms for display or threats in the case of men, as make-up and clothes for sex appeal in the case of women. This last may be disputed, but every woman knows and each man can decide for himself what effect it has upon him. Yet the exception is not purely human—color is seen and appreciated by monkeys and by apes. All the tests are positive, and in any case you only have to visit a zoo and look a male mandrill in the face to be convinced. No creature that was color blind could evolve such a glamorous pattern of blue and red—the color is there and has sexual meaning. Yet lower down the scale of primates color vision disappears—the lemurs are without it. So the surprise it seems is this: that in a stock that was and for the most part is color blind, one lately emerging offshoot has somehow reacquired a sense of color. Living in the tree tops probably has had a lot to do with it, but if the sense had never been lost and more time had been available, what magnificent built-in colors we might have had in place of our trimmings and paint.

168

Color, of course, is the least of it. Our mental and emotional life would be dull with only a monochrome world to look at, but we would still be as mammalian as the rest. And, at present, I am not concerned with what is purely human. Except for a few refinements both of reproduction and of sex, there is little to choose between us and any other placental mammal, and this heritage we hold in common is complicated enough.

If we start with a ready-made, fully formed placental mammal we have altogether too much to consider all at once, yet still have to take things one at a time. So I follow my inclination and keep to the path of history. It is as good as any other.

Leaving aside those changes in bone and brain which distinguish even the lowliest egg-laying mammal from any reptile, we find two features that have been revolutionary in their outcome—a body temperature that remains above 85 degrees Fahrenheit, no matter what the air temperature may be, and a skin that has hair, oil and sweat glands in place of scales. These have been the keys to independence and I am concerned not only with the way in which they operate but also with what brought them into being. It means a probing into the distant past with the aid of a modern platypus; and if this seems remote from our common interest, remember this: those sweater girls pictured skating on an ice rink, warm blooded and full breasted, are the outcome. Yet, apart from sex that is sexy, I feel a fascination in this speculative dropping of a plumb line into time in search for the steps which we have climbed.

The swampy, warm, humid coal forest period gave way to the drier Permian period; and primitive conifers grew in place of tree ferns, while early reptiles laid their new-

fangled eggs equipped with yolk and shell. Water requirements were brought to a minimum, and thick horny scales
prevented water loss by evaporation through the skin.
Everything seemed set for the great age of reptiles—the
Mesozoic age that lasted through the Triassic, Jurassic and
most of the Cretaceous periods, more than one hundred million years—when something happened. Either suddenly or
gradually, a catastrophic change took place, early in Triassic
time. The fossils show the shift, though not its cause. In
the seas great groups of animals that had been well adapted
to their marine world for time out of mind went down to
oblivion; others survived in a tenuous way, and some
splurged forth as though their chance had come at last.
On the land something comparable accompanied the sea
change. A general shift toward the mammalian pattern
took place among the reptiles, and it is at this time that
paleontologists believe the egg-laying mammals came into
existence. The period of cataclysm, however, was of limited
duration and the earth returned to its more normal condition before very long—too late for the sea creatures to re-
cover their old order of existence, but soon enough for
reptiles that remained true to their own nature to go on
with their interrupted act of expansion and dominance.
Most of the mammal-like reptiles were crowded off the stage
and those egg-laying mammals that survived undoubtedly
took to secretive ways. Here is the start of the mammalian
adventure, but just what happened to set it going?

Events such as these, planetary in scale and cosmic at
source, are generally thought to be a consequence, direct or
otherwise, of heat or cold. And it is orthodox to think that
the acquisition and maintenance of warm mammalian blood
was, in origin, a response to the challenge of unusual cold;

for certainly the possession of controlled body warmth enables its owner to exploit or at least survive in the colder regions of the earth. Yet while this last is true, I do not believe the rest. A drop in temperature is rarely dangerous to cold-blooded animals, especially in the sea where temperatures cannot drop below the freezing point. A cooling of the earth, to my mind, cannot account for the marine catastrophe, but a rise in temperature surely can. Even now, when the earth is still within one of its infrequent ice-capped periods and the tropical belt is narrowed, the corals and other creatures of the tropical reefs live remarkably close to their upper thermal death point—a rise of a very few degrees in the surrounding water to a value still below our own blood heat, causes them to die. And it is my own belief that the early Triassic marine catastrophe and the forcing of the primitive mammalian growth on land came not from any chilling but from a passing phase when the planet was for some reason or other being cooked to an unusual degree. It did not have to be very much.

The animals of the sea, leaving aside the seals and whales which are mammals that have gone back to it, have the same temperatures as the water around them. And while as a whole they range from polar waters to the equator, a temperature range from near freezing to about 80 degrees Fahrenheit, no one of them can stand a shift of anything like that extent. A thirty Fahrenheit degree range is about as much as any particular kind of animal can tolerate. The range may be low down on the total scale in the case of polar forms, at the upper end in the tropics, but in any one case if you raise the temperature a few degrees above its upper limit—even if it still seems cold to our skin—a slow coagulation sets in just as if the organism were being

171

cooked, which is not a simile but a fact. I am emphasizing this because we scarcely appreciate the temperature elevation at which we live.

For here is the point. When certain animals left the sea for a life in rivers and lakes, they left a stable environment for one that fluctuated chemically and in temperature to a much greater extent than before. When in turn some of these, including vertebrates, left the freshwaters for the land they not only abandoned water itself, more or less, but entered a world where temperatures could go at times very much higher than they could in either fresh water or the sea. Protoplasm, to lump living matter into a single word, which had been adapted probably from its beginning to limited ranges of the temperature scale found within the ocean, has been forced to adjust itself to higher and higher values. And on the land, when most of the earth has been tropical or subtropical—the more usual state of affairs—living matter has been pushed steadily against its upper limits of toleration. A slow broiling in the sun has undoubtedly been the death of much of it. The problem from the start, once the safety of water was left behind, has been to keep cool enough to live rather than be warm enough to move around. Moreover, the higher the level to which protoplasm becomes adjusted, the narrower, it seems, does the range become— one degree rise and you have a fever, a few more and you die; a degree or so below normal and you are low and out of sorts, a drop of a few more and you go into a coma.

Reptiles like it warm and are sluggish when they are cold —their body temperature fluctuates with their surroundings—but even a desert lizard tossed from the shade of a rock into the open, without time to lighten its color to

172

reflect the light and heat, dies of heat convulsions within a few minutes. And reptiles arose in the first place as a response to desert or semidesert conditions.

This brings me at last to what I believe happened so long ago and forced the issue which resulted in a mammal. Reptiles evolved in the hot dry world that succeeded the steamy coal forests. Their protoplasm became more and more adjusted to the radiant heat and they moved faster the warmer they became. Excess body heat resulting from their own activity and from the sun's rays was radiated from the scaly skin. Then the crisis came. The earth became warmer than ever before, both on land and in the sea, and disaster was the order of the day. Overheated animals either died or moved to cooler regions, or lived on but failed to reproduce; or got rid of their coat of scales and cooled themselves by evaporating water from their skin—gradually, taking numberless generations in which to do it, as the slowly increasing heat sterilized or killed those that could neither escape nor compromise. Here I think is the secret of our mammalian origin. Warmth was thrust upon us and, in order to keep internal heat below the fatal threshold, reptilian scales of armor were discarded, sweat glands evolved to cool the system, hair grew as an insulating coat—insulation from external heat, not cold, just as the Arab wears his mantle in the sun—and oil glands developed to keep skin and hair in good condition. Two more steps and we have our mammal: a central nervous control of the balance between heat production by muscles and heat loss from the skin, so that the internal temperature stays at the level at which the body can act; and the enlargement of the sebaceous or oil-producing glands on the surface of the abdomen

173

to become simple mammary glands for feeding newly hatched young with milk.

This probing for the past has been all too general, however plausible it may seem. Yet it is a past that has survived in antique form into the present, embodied in the platypus and echidna. In the platypus particularly, the dead past comes alive—and the details, I think, are worth the telling; they give flesh and blood to our imagination.

The platypus has specialties which are interesting but I feel are unimportant at this point. The webbed feet and flat tail exist for swimming—and mean no more than those of a beaver; and the flat bill grubs for worms and crayfish in the mud of ponds and streams—and means no more and no less than the bill of a duck. They show what a platypus has become rather than what it may have been all along. Yet a platypus, like any other creature, needs to be looked upon as a whole and not for just what we choose to see, and this account comes from the Badger Creek Sanctuary in Australia.

The soft-furred animal forages at night or twilight, much of the time under water, and spends the rest of the time in earthen burrows sealed at the entrance when once inside. In the mating season, the male and female often swim in a processional courting circle, with the male gripping the tail of the female firmly in his bill—and copulation takes place subsequently in the water. Then the female makes a nest of leaves and grass deep within her burrow—always with wet material—and retires, plugging the road behind her. This is about two weeks after the act of mating, and for some of this time the eggs must have been incubating within the

174

oviduct or the uterus of the mother. The two eggs, each about the size of a sparrow's, are laid within the first few days of retirement and at the time of laying contain an embryo about as well developed as the embryo of a chick thirty-six hours after the onset of incubation, or a human embryo three to four weeks conceived—time becomes relative and biological. And after a week to ten days, during which the mother curls up around her eggs maintaining dampness and warmth from her body, the youngsters hatch. For a few days, probably still nourished by remnants of the original supply of yolk within the abdomen, the young are not fed. Only after the young have hatched and been wiggling for several days, and following vigorous scratching at the mammary area by the mother, does milk begin to flow. Then the suckling commences and continues for about four months before the young are weaned. For the first eleven weeks they are blind and, in the absence of the mother, as cold as any reptile. The heating system of the body, with its controls, apparently is built up slowly during growth. When fully developed, it maintains the platypus at about ten degrees lower than our own body temperature.

So there it is—one of the two egg-laying mammals to persist through two hundred million years. How much of it is new I do not know, but it begins with a skin change and temperature control; it goes on to milk production by skin glands of the abdomen; it involves prolonged maternal care of a very small number of offspring, itself involving the use of a secret hiding place; and food-getting only in the dusk and dark, prolonged to the point of losing the sense of color. The mammal is there, not completely, but unmistakably.

The echidna adds a little more, perhaps another step along the way. The egg is much smaller, no more than one

175

sixth of an inch across, is two or three weeks developed when it is laid, and the mother places it within the small pouch at the base of the abdomen—a delicate procedure at best unless it slips there of its own accord. Milk flows into the pouch from the scattered glands and there the offspring sucks it up. There are no teats in either platypus or echidna —but mammalian milk is flowing and the stage is set for living births.

16. born alive

Mammalian milk and constant heat preceded the birth of naked young. The mammals that laid their eggs belong early in the Age of Reptiles—it is unlikely that many survived unchanged for very long and the marvel is that the platypus and echidna have lived to tell the tale. For one thing led to another, a trend was on the way, and during the period of long eclipse the meek worked out their own salvation.

It is an amazing contrast, for most of mesozoic time great lumbering reptiles shook the ground and floundered in the swamps, while mammals the size of rats and mice kept still by day, lurking among the woods and rocks, foraging for grubs and insects when darkness came, and perfecting themselves as the generations passed. There is little record of what went on; scattered teeth that show how large or small their owners were, and that insects were their food. But we know roughly when the egg-laying mammals first existed, and we know that when the mesozoic age of reptiles came to its mysterious and dramatic end, that both placental mammals and marsupial mammals were abundant and ready to spread across the earth. They left the wings, as the stage began to empty, and took their places. The placentals were more concerned with keeping the egg and embryo within the mother, the marsupials were more intent upon utilizing milk. Of the two, the marsupials were and are the more archaic, and both served to pave the way.

There is no place in this account to speak of the race which followed between the two for inheritance of the earth. The marsupials, it seems, were quicker off the mark, were ready sooner perhaps; but the placentals caught up in the end with better equipment. Now we find marsupials diversified and dominant only in the isolated world of Australia and Tasmania; and elsewhere they persist only in the Americas as primitive and tree-climbing opossums. Yet if egg-laying mammals were the first big step along our way, marsupials of some sort were the next, and they merit our deep attention.

Male and female become more distinct in purely mammalian ways, apart from the basic distinction between ovary and testis. The female develops teats as well as mammary glands, located within her pouch; the male has a penis, and testes that have descended from the original abdominal position near the kidneys into externally situated scrotal sacs. This last is a mammalian feature, not universal by any means, which has been troublesome to mind and body, but there is sense in it, even a condition of survival. And since placental mammals may have evolved from a marsupial type and have most likely inherited the descended testes from this kind, this, I believe, is the place to look for causes.

Once again it appears to be a question of temperature. When organisms are being pushed by external heat up against the temperature limits that their tissues can survive, it rarely happens that all kinds of tissue succumb at once.

178

Some have greater or less tolerance of heat than others, and in different kinds of animals a particular tissue may withstand different limits. Life refuses to be standardized. Yet for some reason cell proliferation and production of spermatozoa appear to be more adversely affected by high temperature than any other tissue, although this seems to be a general mammalian weakness. Birds, which have slightly hotter blood than any mammal, do not have this trouble.

I think we need some facts to start on. Reasons why—generally more interesting than the thing itself—can come after. Most higher mammals, with exceptions that include the largest—whale, elephant, rhinoceros and seal—possess testes which are permanently in the scrotal sacs. Platypus, echidna, armadillo, sloth and some others retain their testes in the original abdominal position. In rodents such as rats and rabbits the testes are in the scrota during the breeding seasons but recede into the abdomen during the intervening periods. When it happens that the testes do not descend, a condition which occasionally turns up not only in man but in dogs, boars, rams, stallions and bulls, the individual nearly always is sterile. It is simply too hot inside.

Many experiments have shown that this is true. Testes of dogs, when surgically replaced in the abdomen before sexual maturity, fail to produce spermatozoa, and the testes of mature animals degenerate within a few months after such procedure. Simple confinement of an adult guinea pig testis within the abdomen results in disorganization within a week, but if it is later replaced in the scrotum it recovers its function of producing spermatozoa. If the guinea pig testis is immature, however, there is development of normal function even after abdominal confinement lasting many months—a fact alone which justifies surgical treatment in boys so afflicted, to bring the testicle into a scrotal position, although it is best done before puberty.

This is one side of it, but everything points to the abdominal temperature of most mammals being too high for the proper growth and activity of the testes. The temperature inside the scrotal sacs of rodents, rams and human beings is anywhere from two to fourteen degrees Fahrenheit lower than the temperature within the abdomen at the time. Wrapping the scrotum of a ram in layers of wool leads to an early degeneration of the testis within; and so does subjecting the testes of guinea pigs for fifteen minutes to a bath no hotter than one you usually enjoy. So it really comes to this—the scrotum, in those mammals including man where it exists, is a temperature-regulating mechanism by virtue of its exposed position, thin walls, and its own response to temperature. Warmth causes a relaxation of a special muscle with resulting removal of the testes from the warmth of the body, while external cold results in its contraction so that the testes are warmed. It is an effective device. And from the point of view of the race it is better to be vulnerable than sterile. Farmers keep their bulls outside the barn, where the breezes blow, to make them more virile. It is the same idea.

Yet the male mammalian situation is far from being uniform. The egg-laying mammals and those peculiar and primitive placentals, the sloths and armadillos, retain the testes permanently within the abdomen. Both groups have body temperatures within the safety zone, and sperm production can proceed without descent. The marsupial mammals and, among the placental mammals, the carnivora, the herbivora, and monkeys, apes and men all have permanently descended scrotal testes—and normal body temperatures that fall within the range of 95-103° F. Elephants and whales are special cases—their testes are undescended and we do not know the reason why; they are not the easiest animals to investigate.

This leaves us with three groups of small-bodied but equally hot-blooded placental mammals—the rodents, bats, and the primitive shrew. In all of these, the testes are kept within the safety of the abdomen when active sperm production is not required; but the testes descend into the cooler scrotal sacs during the breeding times when spermatozoa must be actively produced. In the woodchuck, for instance, the testes descend by April, but reascend by July and remain in the abdomen throughout summer, fall, and winter. This seems a sensible arrangement too, as long as the inactive testes can stand the higher internal temperature. After all, it is where they belong, and the exposed position is actually a penalty paid for not keeping the body temperature quite cool enough.

I can accept things as they are without much difficulty— under the circumstances I can see no alternative—but I am puzzled by how this situation came to be. It happened at some time during the long mammalian suppression and was probably a response to intolerable and prolonged environmental heat. A dangerous situation called for a risky venture. And it is curious that we find more of a clue in primitive placentals like the insectivorous shrews and bats than we do even in the pouched marsupials. In both shrews and certain bats there is a seasonal displacement of the testes that does not result in extrusion into external scrotal sacs but does go far enough to make contact with a thin portion of the posterior abdominal wall where body heat is less intense. It is very likely that this is a survival of an

181

early state of affairs—the further step to passage through the inguinal canals into external skin pouches follows easily and logically, almost like a hernia, and may well have been made independently in marsupials and in the less primitive placental mammals. A shift of the testes to the coolest part of the abdominal cavity prevented sterility. I can see that all those early mammals, whether marsupial or placental, that failed to save themselves from heat-induced sterility simply failed to propagate their kind. What is remarkable is that this did not lead to racial extinctions—in fact, perhaps it did, except in a few that for some obscure reason had their testes already out of place. And I cannot see how any heat-produced emergency could possibly cause a shift in the position of the testes. Once the heat caught up it would be much too late, and it seems to me there must have been some lucky accidents somewhere along the way. The answer is not clear, but at least it leaves you with something to think about.

If mammalian males have suffered tribulation in the interests of paternity, so have females for the sake of maternity. Eggs that are laid must be protected, in the case of egg-laying mammals both from enemies and from cold. The mother must stay around until they hatch, and even after that must feed and coddle them till they are grown enough to keep themselves warm and find their own food. Birds have managed to do all this in the safety of their nests. Having wings, they could find sanctuaries beyond the reach of reptiles and, later on, of mammals. But the mammal itself must have been handicapped at once. This is shown I think by that fact that the platypus is the single survivor of those that had warm blood but still laid their eggs upon the ground. Even the echidna succeeds in carrying its egg around and is not tied down and exposed to the dangers of staying in one particular spot. The original mammalian adventure, in evolving controlled body warmth and milk glands for suckling, involved taking care of a small number of precious eggs and young throughout several months, and doing so in a safe retreat. Freedom was lost, either to get enough food, perhaps, or to run from an enemy without abandoning offspring. If you must raise a family where the wolf not only is at the door but is apt to get inside, you must live like the Eskimos and both young and old must keep on the move. And the simplest way the mammals could find to get out of their predicament was not to lay their eggs at all. You can see it starting in echidna.

There is little doubt about what happened—after all we are here to prove it. Platypus and echidna have inherited the reptilian egg and it is with this we begin. There is no need to make the two Australians carry all the burden. Follow the egg of a reptile—or a bird's or a platypus', whichever you like—from the ovary to the laying of the egg in a nest. To start with we have the ovum, large and yolky but without egg white or shell. It escapes by rupture from the surface of the ovary and somehow travels the short distance to the funnel of an oviduct. On entering the funnel it becomes fertilized or remains an unfertilized egg forever after and then journeys down the tube. For much of the way, simple glands pour out albumen, wrapping the egg in layers, forming the white of egg around it. Then the junction of the oviduct and uterus is reached, the egg in its envelopes pauses, and a calcareous shell is formed around the whole, partly permeable to water in the case of reptiles and platy-

183

pus, thicker and impermeable in the case of birds. It is ready to be laid, with others that may have been stored ahead of it.

This is the setting. If the egg of an echidna means anything, it suggests that the egg became pretty small while still possessing yolk and shell, so that it could be hatched more readily in a pouch. Its diameter of one-sixth of an inch includes the whole and the ovum within is only about half the size. It is not too great a step to the marsupial state—one easily conceived, at all events. For in the marsupial mammals, whether Australian or American, we find that the egg is smaller still: it ripens in the ovary and enters the oviduct when no more than one-hundredth of an inch across, small enough by any scale yet large enough still to contain some yolk. It is fertilized in the tube as before and, as before, it pauses when it descends as far as the uterus. Only now there is a difference. There is no longer any gland to lay a shell around it, and while it lingers it continues to divide and grow—and the outer surface of the yolk sac of the embryo makes contact with the uterine wall and gains nourishment from it. This works for a time. However, the expanding but nearly yolkless yolk sac fails to hold its own and, ready or not, the embryo is born. In the Virginia opossum the young are born after only twelve to thirteen days, in a remarkably immature state. As such, they have to make their way to the entrance of the maternal pouch and fasten themselves to the teats. Milk is then forcibly pumped into them until they are able to help themselves—and the milk-sustained growth and development continue for about three months. This is reasonably typical of the marsupial world and leads to interests somewhat

184

beyond our present scope. I am concerned with it here more as a stage on the way to full placental state.

There must have been a parting of the ways. Marsupials experimented up to a point in methods of holding developing eggs at the uterine station, but none of them carried it very far. Their main emphasis has been in the direction of making the maximum use of the milk and protecting the young while they nurse. Placental mammals took the other path and concentrated on means of keeping the embryo for longer periods within the uterus. Eggs became even smaller and almost without yolk, and the range of size now runs from about one four-hundredth of an inch across for such as hamsters and mice to about one two-hundredth for horse and man. A system has been evolved in the uterus, where the old shell gland used to be, which is the secret of our success if not of our existence. It takes us back for a moment to the reptilian egg, for this is a case of one invention leading to another.

I am an embryologist by profession and I may overestimate the general interest in these eggs of vertebrates; yet, I do not think so. They hold the mystery of life, and I doubt that any single event in this universe has more content and implication than the expansion of an invisible speck of protoplasm into a monkey or a man. And so much of the history of vertebrates, which is our own history too, has been the history of eggs: the shift from the sea to the rivers, when eggs changed from microscopic specks to eggs like those of frogs, which can divide without external aid into more than a million cells; the shift from freshwater to the land, when eggs became relatively enormous and confined within calcareous shells; and the shift from eggs that are laid to eggs that are kept, with loss of the shell and the yolk. Each step sets the stage for the next.

The reptilian egg, which you can see just as well in the egg of a hen, is a marvel of adaptation. For you cannot enclose a large yolky egg within a rigid shell without serious consequences, no matter how necessary such a shell may be. Confinement created difficulties, which were successfully overcome or we wouldn't be here to talk about them. One of these was that the embryo could not grow freely from the surface of the mass of yolk. The shell formed a ceiling overhead and, in the process of sinking down in place of rising up, the embryo became enfolded by membranes which made a sort of water jacket around it. If you open a hen's egg after a week or ten days of incubation you can see the chick within its jacket—the amnion—not only well protected but rhythmically rocked by contractions of the membranes. The other two major problems were solved as one—storing of watery waste and obtaining the all-essential oxygen. A sac grew out from the hinder end of the embryo which did double duty in holding waste and supplying a large surface rich in blood vessels for respiration. The amniotic jacket and the allantoic sac were necessary for embryonic life to proceed within the shell, and the combination of it all enabled the reptiles to conquer the land. This is the developing egg that the mammal has retained within its uterus, without the shell and without the yolk, and it always seems to me surprising that the jacket and the sac, which in a sense were created by yolk and shell, survive the loss of their creators.

This is what happens. It holds for a bat, it holds for a whale, and it holds for a man. The minute fertilized egg which travels down the oviduct, dividing as it goes, reaches

186

the uterus and by one means or another becomes implanted in its wall. Development of the amnion and of the allantoic sac is precocious. The amnion becomes the water jacket, just as it used to be, although we know it better in the mammal as the fetal membranes. The sac, however, is a sac no longer, but is a solid growth rich in blood vessels which interlock with those of the maternal uterus and serves as the placenta which designates our kind, serving to obtain all nourishment for the embryo from the mother and, simultaneously, to eliminate all waste. When at last the placenta begins to fail in its task of keeping pace with fetal growth, separation commences and birth takes place.

This is the heart of it, but the physiological mechanisms involved are intricate and almost infinitely elaborate. Yet there is one question which overrides the rest: what is the real relationship between the parent and its egg? I find the answer startling and almost shocking.

Briefly it is this. The egg and the embryo that it becomes is as determined a parasite as anything that goes by such a name; but of all the possible and impossible places in the body where development can take place, the uterus alone needs preparation. I suppose it ought not to be surprising since this used to be the last stop before the egg was laid.

The facts speak for themselves. Here are a few experiments. Fertilized guinea pig eggs removed from the oviducts and placed within the outer chamber of the eye, where they can be observed with a microscope through the clear cornea, go on dividing and developing and actually become implanted on the iris. They do just as well when placed within the eye of a male mouse instead of a female guinea pig. And it often happens in rabbits, and can be made to happen in rats, that fertilized eggs escape from the oviduct back

187

into the abdominal cavity. It makes no difference; they attach themselves to the mesenteries or anywhere on the peritoneal lining and live out the full term of their development—only, of course, they can't get out. I once saw a rabbit that had young embryos in the uterus and a set of fully developed but dead and partly resorbed young in the cavity of the abdomen. There is no doubt at all that the mammalian embryo, whatever its kind, grows anywhere it can and takes what it wants from the maternal tissues, no matter what the cost may be to the mother.

This is only one side of the question. The other concerns the uterus. Under normal circumstances fertilized eggs seem happy enough to settle there—yet it takes some arranging and the ovary takes a part in it.

The chemical controls in a higher vertebrate like ourselves and the rest of those that walk about, are built somewhat like a house of cards, one upon another—decidedly impressive, but the balance must be good. Far back at the start of things, as we still find in most of the lowlier types of animal life, an ovary is nothing more than an egg- or ova-producing gland, consisting of cells that grow to form the ova, each surrounded by cells that help them grow— the follicle cells. In vertebrates in general, and the more so as we climb the ladder, intervening tissue separates the ova, each within its follicle, from one another; most of the sex hormones of the body come from this follicular and connecting tissue and from somewhat similar tissue in the male. When we come to mammals, the large balloon-like follicle still forms around the ovum and is essential for its growth, but the ovum within the follicle has shrunk to microscopic dimensions. When ovulation occurs and the ovum escapes from its enveloping follicle, a hole is left behind which not

188

only fills up with the disorganized cells of the follicle, but the cellular mass continues to grow until it is large and obvious to the naked eye. It is called the *corpus luteum*—the name given to this yellow body by older anatomists—and it manufactures and sends out a hormone of its own.

At the beginning of this century, investigators devised various experiments on rabbits to find out what these yellow bodies in the ovary were there for, and they showed at once that if they were left alone pregnancies occurred in the normal way, but if removed, leaving the rest of the ovary intact, pregnancy failed, no matter what the circumstances. The next step was the discovery that as long as a *corpus luteum* was present in the ovary, the wall of the uterus would respond as though it were co-operating to form a placenta even to bits of glass or a cotton thread placed there instead of eggs. To cut the story short, the yellow bodies form only after the ova have left and started on their way; the hormone they secrete reaches the uterus wall by way of the circulating blood long before the eggs are ready to implant themselves, and the uterine tissue reacts in such a way as to welcome them, by secreting liquid nourishment and responding to actual contact—otherwise, it is unusually unresponsive and rejects them. And here is one further proof that has come to light recently—a rabbit with three embryos in the nineteenth day of pregnancy was operated on in such a way that one of the three escaped into the abdominal cavity while the other two embryos remained in the uterus; at the same time the ovaries with their yellow bodies were removed. The result? The two left in the uterus died while the one in the abdomen completed its development.

So the picture, I think, is clear. If the mammalian egg

was to be retained in the body throughout its development, it had to be kept where the embryo could finally escape. The uterus, where the shelled eggs used to be stored, was the logical place. But that was already an anteroom to the external world, and reluctant tissue had to be made even more responsive than most if eggs were to implant there successfully. The system worked out is neat: the yellow body forms as the result of the egg's departure—it is a built-in timepiece itself, and any chemical it sends into the blood would serve as a signal; but the special kind which is formed is one to which uterine tissue responds in a certain expectant way, which is part of the chemical wisdom of the body and far beyond my depth.

17. masculine and feminine

Sex cells are as clearly set apart from one another as any two kinds of cells can be—there is never any confusion whether they are eggs or sperm. In the simpler animals an individual is male or female, sometimes both, according to the kind of sex cells it produces; you know its sex by the sex glands it possesses—there is little else to go on. In birds and mammals and other vertebrates, in which hormones play so great a part, the primary sex relating to egg production or sperm production may be overshadowed by what the hormones do to the so-called secondary sexual structures and to the patterns of behavior. Sex is no longer a simple, clear-cut difference between the two kinds of individuals of a species. In human beings and many animals the lines are smudged and it is a case of more or less, not either or. A man has a deep voice and grows a beard, but he has nipples too. And it used to be that whistling girls were frowned upon as being neither one thing nor the other. The world grows complicated and so do we.

The trouble goes back to the beginning of things—not in this case to a distant time but to the start of life for the individual. And, whether of fish or human, the problem is basically the same. The reproductive gland at first is in a neutral condition and can be influenced to grow into either an ovary or a testis, or perhaps both. As a rule the sperm either brings to the egg the extra unit of the sex factor and then the embryo which develops, together with all its tissues, is female; or the sperm lacks this unit and the outcome is male. This is the usual way of favoring the development of either the male or the female tissue of the

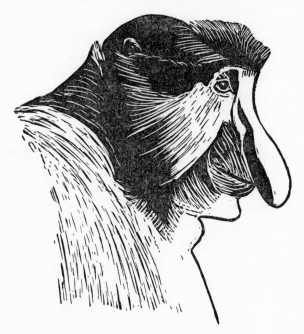

Male of Nasal monkey of Borneo.

original reproductive gland, but in some cases it is barely enough to tip the balance, while in others one of the two sides is heavily loaded. Yet, no matter whether the inherited determiners are weak or strong, sex hormones can override their influence if enough of them are introduced.

Salamanders have had their sex changed in both directions, from male to female and from female to male, by hormones from more mature reproductive glands of the opposite sex transplanted into their bodies. Frog tadpoles, left alone, pass through a neutral stage before their glands become either ovaries or testes, and eventually they become male and female in approximately equal numbers; but the inherited constitution supplied by sperm and egg is very readily overridden, and, as we have seen, a rise in temperature can alone swing almost all of a group of tadpoles into masculinity; or if frog eggs are too slow in passing from the ovaries down the tubes to be laid and fertilized, maleness predominates among the offspring. The developmental controls are delicate chemical mechanisms and they are readily deranged. Embryos can be influenced to change to either direction, but in fully grown animals it seems much easier to force a change from female to male than from male to female.

We have seen what happens in birds when the single ovary is removed: there is no replacement of the ovary, but the rudimentary testis on the other side grows to maturity and what was a hen becomes a cock. And by a slightly different means the same sort of thing can happen to a fish. Siamese fighting fish, the bettas, who mate and pair off in an elaborate manner to build bubble nests together, show this and a great deal besides. When a female has had her ovaries removed, she loses all the normal phases

193

of her reproductive behavior and also her attractiveness to the male. Sex appeal is a subtle thing—not merely a matter of shape but the way the shape moves, an indefinable invitation that even a fish can recognize.

And in the case of a betta that has lost her allure through operation, an injection of ovarian extract with its sex hormone restores both her normal instincts and her appeal. A slight change in chemistry can work wonders. Yet if no such compensation is offered and the victim is left alone with her condition, the reproductive glands may regenerate a testis, though never an ovary, and before very long she assumes the characteristic fins and behavior of the male— even to the extent of normal mating with a female. The turnabout results from the presence of a small amount of neutral reproductive gland where the ovaries had been. The individual was a female only so long as there were ovaries and female sex hormones.

If female hormone makes a lady seductive, male hormone makes a male show the stuff he's made of. Chickens as a rule do not attempt to mate until they are five or six months old; but two-day male chicks who received daily injections of male hormone began to stretch and crow on the fourth day of their existence, with all the gusto of roosters. On the eighth day, after six injections, they began to fight and flap their wings. After eight injections they tried to mate with female chicks, and carried the deep red wattle of the mature cock.

Male hormone when injected will even overrule the actions of a normal female. Jewel fish so treated often try to copulate even without the necessary organ, although the organ grows later; and it is interesting that the change in instinct and behavior precedes any anatomical development

194

—mind responds quicker than the body. Female swordtail fishes behave in a masculine way under male hormone influence, grow a sword, and gain in prestige. And while the same hormone will make a hen crow and female canaries sing like males, it also raises their position in the social scale. Masculinity and aggressiveness go hand in hand.

Yet, here's the rub. Ovaries produce the female hormone but they also produce the male, while testes manufacture not only the male but the female as well. There is more of one than another in either case and it is the proportion of one to the other that counts and makes male and female what they are. Bearded ladies are females who failed to get the mixture right.

The woman with the beard and the man with the squeaky voice have too much male hormone on the one hand and not enough on the other, but whoever you are and whatever you are, both kinds are circulating in your blood and the way you act is the outcome of these and others besides. You can see something of the way they blend in the sexual life of the laughing gulls—those beautiful birds that develop black head feathers and red beaks, red eye margins and red legs as a nuptial dress in the breeding season, male and female alike; and can scare the wits out of you at night with their demoniacal laughter, the more so when it is unfamiliar and you cannot see who makes it. My spine tingles yet, after many years.

Their sexual behavior includes postures and also calls common to both sexes, although each sex has its own distinctive behavior in addition. When male hormone is injected into either sex it brings about all those calls and postures common to them both, and also those you expect of the breeding male. But female hormone injected into either sex stimulates the suppliant, subordinate behavior normally confined to the female and essential for successful mating, consisting of begging for food with lowered head and also of the proper response to the sex call of the male. Neither a bird, nor a fish, nor a human being is completely male or completely female. Life would be so much less interesting if they were, and the battle of the sexes could never arise where all aggression was on one side and all submission on the other. Foregone conclusions are dull indeed.

Behavior isn't everything. Sex is anatomical as well, and sex hormones may interfere with much more than a state of mind. It all depends upon the time at which they act: a young embryo may be vastly influenced, but an older individual may remain anatomically unaffected. The experimental method is to give heavy doses of the hormone to a pregnant rat—if it is heavy enough, some of it will pass the barriers of the placenta and reach the embryo within the womb. Female embryos—those with ovaries already formed at the time male sex hormone reaches them—are born in consequence without nipples but with male copulatory organs; they have ovaries but are otherwise male. Male embryos subjected to female hormones by the same method are born with nipples present but no copulatory organs. They are anatomically female although fundamentally male; the testes are still testes, though they no longer descend into scrotal sacs.

All this, of course, is an abnormal state of affairs, because embryos as a rule are safe from such interference; and they do not manufacture sex hormones in any quantity themselves until their anatomical nature is already well established. Yet the knowledge so acquired helps us understand another situation: apparent change of sex in human beings.

196

One of the most curious things about sex hormones is that the sex glands are not the only tissues that produce them. Tremendous amounts of female sex hormones are manufactured by the placenta and excreted by the mother during pregnancy—not only in rats and mice, but in humans too—together with some male hormone. Usually it doesn't matter because these hormones are produced too late to do any harm, but this is not always true.

The danger exists chiefly for the male. A female embryo is not harmed by additional female hormone—the child may be more feminine than usual at an early age, and everybody's pleased. But the same female hormone may seriously upset the masculine development, so that boy babies may be born that are truly males but under the impact of the feminizing hormone look superficially like females—and are reared as such. About one person in a thousand is like this —males unconsciously masquerading as women. But they have the muscular strength of men and on two occasions have won a women's competition at the Olympic games; now entrants have to undergo a physical examination before the event.

Individuals of this kind are unfortunate, at least those that are genuine and, I suppose also, those that are not. And they may be unfortunate in two degrees. Most of these boys in petticoats have more or less sterile, undescended testes, an imperfect organ, well-developed breasts, an unbroken voice and no beard. The female hormone of the placenta caught them at an early stage, with resulting confusion. The other group, which is not so common but is more likely to get into the news, consists of those cases you hear of girls changing into men—voice, beard, breasts and sexual interest take on the pattern of the male, usually in

late adolescence. The placental female hormone had its
say, but not quite so precociously; it ceases at birth in any
case, and slowly the male hormone of the testis swings the
system back to normal as far as may be possible; what was
thought to have been a girl was really a boy, and Nature
corrects the error. It is disconcerting, to say the least,
whatever the final outcome, for minds can be feminized by
society as well as by hormones, and correction of a mistake
generally leaves the work of erasure. Growing from an egg
is a hazardous performance and most of us are luckier than
we realize.

18. sex, cycles and

seasons

To have effective equipment for reproduction is one thing, to use it at the right time is another. Breeding must be adjusted to the nature of the external world—birds must hatch their nestlings and mammals bring forth their young at the proper season, when there is food enough and warmth enough to make raising them not too difficult. The time of emergence from the shell or the womb is the crucial one, and all else must conform to it—the growth of the reproductive glands and the time for mating must be adjusted to make it right or it is all in vain. Only in the more domesticated mammals, the dogs and cats, rabbits and humans, warm and well fed throughout the year, can breeding occur at any time. The rest are seasonal, not merely in their reproduction but in their capacity to reproduce. Ovaries and testes wax and wane in a rhythmical way in a regular cycle—in hormone production as well as the production of eggs and sperm. In some manner their cycles of growth and maturity are brought into relationship with events in the outside world, and the controls work through the small pituitary gland that lies beneath the brain; one part of it belongs to the brain itself.

Here lies the gateway whereby the external universe pouring in through the senses reaches into the chemical controls. Cosmic or earthly clocks call the signals and, through basic pathways in the brain, set off pituitary secretions which may bring about the growth of gonads or even start an ovulation. Rain, or perhaps humidity, starts the cycle in Australian frogs and cockatoos and in American toads, but more often than not it is light—moonlight, ultraviolet light or the light we see from the sun. European night jars, which fly and feed by night alone, lay a pair of eggs during the last quarter of the moon so that the chicks can be reared during the following full moon when hunting can continue all night long. It is more than a matter of laying two eggs, for the growth of the eggs is controlled as well, and the more I think about it the more impressed I get by this interweaving rhythm of a satellite and some eggs.

Most of the larger birds and mammals breed but once a year, and almost always in the spring in the temperate regions of the earth. The reasons are obvious, for the time is short when food is plentiful, and birds in any case must grow to their full size before they can fly and fully take care of themselves. Growth is violent as long as it lasts.

The farther north in the north temperate zone and the farther south in the south temperate, the later in the spring or summer the breeding season becomes, at the rate of twenty to thirty days for each ten degrees of latitude. This, of course, is a general statement, and while there is a lot of truth in it I think it is typical of its kind. It is all very well to see the wood in spite of the trees, but the trees must be

200

kept in view within the larger vision. When we move toward the equator, the differences between one kind of bird and another become apparent. Hawks, swifts and nightjars lay their eggs earlier and earlier as the equator is approached, and so do the host of passerine birds, although to a lesser extent. But wading birds, ducks and gulls breed later and later toward the equator, just as they do as they approach the poles. And there is the laysan albatross which, when it breeds in Hawaii, twenty degrees north of the equator, does so at the time of the southern spring when the rest of its kind is breeding. We seem to hear a double beat of inborn internal rhythms and the external compulsion of the sun and the seasons. Yet, in the end, the influence of the environment overpowers what internal breeding rhythm there may be if the two should be in conflict. Life is adaptable, through generations if not through individuals. Spotted deer introduced from India into Europe continued to produce their offspring in midwinter, which was fatal, but after a while they adjusted and young were born at a more suitable time. The spring-breeding English song birds of the northern hemisphere, which have been taken to Australia and New Zealand, all breed now in the southern spring. The environment asserts itself, although somewhere inside the body some tissue or organ undergoes a physiological rhythm with a periodicity of about one year. A seasaw action between pituitary stimulation of the ovary and ovarian hormone inhibition of the pituitary has been suggested but, while a relationship of this kind does exist, as an explanation it leaves too many questions unanswered. One way of escape—and I think it is escapism pure and simple—is to assume that everything depends upon a self-sustained rhythmic activity in the

201

pituitary gland alone. This is equivalent to shelving the question.

Light plays its part, particularly in the case of birds, although the chain of events is none too clear. If birds are kept awake in autumn for longer periods than usual by adding periods of artificial light to normal daytime, both ovaries and testes increase in size and may mature. In the junco it may be the wakefulness and the activity that goes with it that makes the pituitary stimulate the gonad; in the starling it looks more like the light itself. And certainly in the ferret, which is a mammal and not a bird, absence of light prevents the usual sexual development associated with the spring.

The eye is all-important to a bird, and whether it is the sight of a nesting place, or the sexual posturing of a pair, or the bright colors and songs of display, the stimulus of light sifts, by some means or another, through the brain to reach the glands. In the birds, the female is stimulated partly by the world around her and partly by the antics and appearance of the male. The first concerns more the growth of her eggs, the second their ovulation, although the situation is very variable and considerably mixed.

I find it difficult to dissociate sex and reproduction of the birds from the question of migrations, for they are obviously involved; though what concerns us here is not the mystery of navigation but the timing of the impulse that starts the birds upon their journeys, a mystery, in some instances, just as great. The Australian mutton bird, one of the shearwaters, spends most of the year spread out over the vastness of the north Pacific, from the equator to Bering Strait; but in November of each year they arrive at certain small islands off the Australian coast, virtually by the millions, more or less ready to breed. Apart from the fact of their convergence upon pin point breeding places, and the means by which they find their way, there is the fact that they arrive almost all at once, starting from places thousands of miles apart. There must be some sort of environmental clock that sets them going, but what it is I have no idea.

Male stork greeting female on arrival at nest.

203

Yet, in migrating birds such as the swallows that we know more about, that winter in the southern hemisphere, the beginning of the movement north to the breeding areas is preceded by active growth of their gonads. Whether the rhythm that starts such growth is internal or of external origin, there is little doubt that the nervous excitement that comes with the increasing flow of sex hormones is all-important. There are many ways of lighting a fire, but once one is lit beneath a man he gets up and starts to travel. A bird is not so different. As sex glands mature, nervous energy increases, and it may be directed into many channels besides mating and reproduction, although other activities may not be unrelated. So when the restlessness and tension mounts above a certain threshold, the birds take wing on their breeding migration.

It is hard to measure the nervous state of a bird and to compare one occasion with another, and the so-called sexual drive is more readily estimated in a rat. During the quiescent period of her sexual cycle, a female rat kept in a revolving drum may turn the drum perhaps one or two hundred times in a six-hour period, but when growth of the ovarian follicles nears completion and the time for mating approaches, the frequency of her movements is amazing; the drum may be turned four thousand times in the same length of time. The activity here, of course, is normally directed toward the finding of a mate, but at bottom it is the same—a keying-up of the whole nervous system of the individual in response to the release of sexual hormones. The energy made available may find a mate for a rat, drive a swallow across the equator, or make a starling sing. And the starling, the British starling in particular, has a case history worth a little notice.

204

In late summer, when the size of the gonads is at a minimum, song is quiet, nest-visiting rare, and communal life dominates the scene. In autumn, the gonads begin to grow, song becomes loud and long, nest-hole visiting becomes common, and birds associate in pairs. By the end of December, communal roosting gives way to nest-hole roosting in pairs, and in February the building of nests commences. When, in April, the gonads are fully developed, the sexual patterns of behavior are completely formed—breeding occurs, eggs are incubated, and the young are fed. When the gonads shrink, in June, all this reproductive activity comes to an end. The pairs break up and lose their attachment to the nesting sites, and the strident communal life starts all over again.

There is little doubt that the sexual and reproductive behavior keep in step with the growth of gonads, both in male and female, although the relationship is subtle. The gonads swell as long as the pituitary calls the tune, while the birds behave according to the tensions produced by the hormones sent out by the ovary and the testes, with an intensity of response which increases with the mounting concentration. Yet, in the end, it is the brain, or part of it, which calls forth the pattern of behavior, responding in turn to the sexual hormones on the one hand and the external surroundings on the other. The circuit closes, and reproduction starts.

The bird is useful here, not entirely for its own sake but as a back drop for a mammal. Each has handicaps and advantages which play their part. Birds as a whole have lost their sense of smell but have color vision carried to its zenith; they can fly, it is true, but they have lost whatever use their forelegs may once have had as arms, while their hind legs are little more than perching stilts. This is caricature to some extent, I know, but not untrue. When you add to it the fact that birds in general have no external genital organs to aid in mating, you see the situation they contend with. The urge to perform the act of mating comes only at the end of more or less prolonged hormonal and psychic stimulation and the sexes need to be in harmony. Yet, even more than that, the act itself demands complete co-operation in view of all the circumstances of anatomy. Unless synchronization of the emotional sexual state of a mating pair is brought to perfection, the mating fails. Everything must be right: a water hen that mates with ease upon its mating platform has trouble in a meadow, even when desire is mutual and intense. Sight and perception compose the picture in relation to the sex cells and the hormones.

Such is the world of the bird. The mammalian world is somewhat different. If we leave ourselves and our poor relations outside for a while, mammals in general walk upon four legs instead of balancing precariously on two, have a sense of smell that holds them down to earth, and are color blind. External genital structures facilitate the sexual act. Fertilization of the eggs is easier to promote, sight is less important and synchronizing of emotional states less exquisite, while hormones play a greater part in governing the situation.

Altogether, the system is most efficient. Maternal milk leads to maternal solicitude, but the connubial bliss so widespread among the birds is the exception, not the rule, among the mammals. And rarely does a male play a part in anything but mating. This leads to promiscuity, and can lead to trouble. Generalizing is unsafe and only the particular usually has much meaning; one or two instances will illustrate my point.

When animals reproduce by pairs, in close association both before and after mating, the sex ratio of equal numbers of the sexes is sensible and not wasteful. When females do all the actual work of reproduction, when promiscuity is the rule and a single male can take the place of many, most of the males become redundant. Racially speaking, it is a wasteful process to produce as many males as females, and where males do not assert themselves they may suffer. The female hamster tends to turn upon her partner after mating and may kill him. After all, what may be good for an individual may be bad for the race, and food consumed by superabundant males may impoverish a community. In rodent society, the majority of the males have little more value than drones in a hive.

In other ways the habits of the species and the reproductive cycle of the female may mitigate against the forming of any bonds between the sexes. A lion and lioness may mate for life, hunting prey and rearing cubs in close association. Appetite is subordinate to emotion and intelligence. But with the fisher, until recently a common mammal in this land, it is another matter. The female brings forth her pups in April in seclusion. No male is allowed around, for his desire for meat, it seems, would make him eat his young. He isn't pushed out of the den for he never gets into it. The complicating factor here is need for timing birth. April is the proper season, but the young require a full twelve months within the womb before they can be born, and months of suckling afterward. So, after birth has taken place, the female comes into heat at once, and one night or two in April goes out to find a mate. That is all he sees of her or knows of reproduction, for she returns to take care of her family with her next brood already started. All the male is required to do is to be alive in April and not be too hard to find.

It is important to a mammal as it is to a bird that its young shall enter the world at a time when the environment gives the best chance to survive. For annual breeders, birth occurs in springtime so that the summer can be employed for finding food and growing up. Even in the male the environment may take a hand in seeing that this is so. In the snowshoe rabbit the testes in January are small and abdominal; they increase in size in February and descend into the scrotal sacs at the end of the month, reaching their maximum weight in March. This is the onset of the breeding season and the male remains functional as such until July. Then the testes decrease in size, and in September, when their weight is lowest, they return to the abdomen. If the animal walked around on its hind legs like a man you would think gravity and changing weight were at the bottom of it, but when you have all four feet on the ground the load is where it was meant to be; only the bipeds get sagging insides. Yet in the snowshoe rabbit the growth of the testes determines their position; while the increasing hours of daylight of late winter work through the eyes and pituitary to bring about the growth. If the amount of light is reduced, the growth of the testes is delayed.

The female is not so different. Some have mated and are ready to litter in April, most of them in May, and the season then declines through June. Yet if both sexes are exposed throughout most of the winter to eighteen hours of light a day, the mating season is advanced by at least a month. Masking the eyes prevents this, while changing from eighteen to nine hours of light a day causes both the ovaries and the testes to regress. The environment dominates the organism in this instance, and probably even more precisely in the fisher. This is true, too, of the English fox which ovulates spontaneously in January and does not come into heat at any other time of the year. It all depends on how ingrained internal rhythms happen to be. The common rat is nocturnal and light has little meaning in the present sense, except that the period of heat, which comes on every four to six days, usually lasts from ten to eighteen hours. Generally it begins at dusk, or a little sooner or later, and lasts through the night. Only the dark is safe. But what is remarkable is that an experimental reversal of the hours of light and darkness causes a shift of the onset of heat to the new time of darkness. Yet the regular rhythm goes on when darkness is continual. It can be shifted to conform to the world outside, but it cannot be destroyed, and the rhythm itself cannot be changed.

When light affects so many, it seems to me surprising that the domestic rabbit does not respond in any way to changes. During the breeding season, in the absence of the male, the doe remains in heat almost indefinitely, with wave after wave of egg follicles maturing in the ovary and each persisting in condition to be shed for a period of a week or more. If mating is permitted, the follicles rupture within ten hours and the eggs enter the oviducts to be fertilized. The stimulus seems to be emotional since intense excitement, such as the act of mounting or being mounted by another doe, evokes it. Within an hour of mating, the pituitary releases sufficient hormone to cause an ovulation, so that pregnancy is certain.

It is the fate of a domesticated animal to be experimented

with, and the rabbit has had more than its fair share. Yet we know in consequence that the eggs have a fertile life of not more than six hours. If sperm have not reached them within that time, they cannot be fertilized. The timing system accordingly is important, but since spermatozoa can survive within the oviducts for up to eighteen hours, they are still potent at the time the eggs arrive. And it takes an enormous number of spermatozoa to start with to ensure that enough will get to the upper reaches of the tubes. A buck emits some two hundred million on each occasion, a number which seems astronomical and is about the same for man. But if does are inseminated artificially with less than a million spermatozoa, fertilization of the eggs is doubtful. If less than ten thousand are introduced, it does not occur at all. You get some idea of the difficulties of travel when you consider that in the case of the rat, spermatozoa numbering only from seven to one hundred and seventy have been found in the upper areas of the tubes, under normal mating conditions. And it appears likely that in the human, too, similar small numbers alone reach the fertilization regions out of the millions that start. The problems of male infertility raise their head at this point, and books have been written about them.

There are hazards all the way along the line, and they apply to eggs as well as sperm. The elephant shrew, no elephant in size though large for a shrew, sheds about one hundred and twenty eggs at a time, but only one or two become implanted. And rabbit eggs must be fertilized just as they enter the funnels of the oviducts, for as they continue their journey they acquire a layer of albumen which spermatozoa cannot penetrate.

I think we know more concerning rabbit eggs than we

do of the eggs of any other kind of mammal. And, for obvious reasons, we know almost as little of human eggs as we do of any other. But there are many ways, including a little electrical stimulation of the head, to make a doe's pituitary release its ovulation hormone and cause the ovaries to shed their eggs. What it amounts to is this: considering everything, we can obtain either unfertilized or fertilized eggs of the domestic rabbit almost at will—and much of the study of the development of the live mammalian egg has been of these. One of the startling outcomes is that the unfertilized eggs, when placed in a sustaining salt solution, start to divide and develop—and some of these when reimplanted in the uterus of another doe have gone on to complete their development, finally to be born as young rabbits. Actually, of course, it should not be any more surprising to find virgin birth a possibility in a rabbit than to find spontaneous development of eggs in the water flea or experimentally stimulated development of unfertilized eggs of sea urchins and starfish. It brings us back to a basic fact, that fertilization is more essential for evolution than it is for reproduction.

Speaking of spermatozoa, the little brown bat that flutters through the twilight east of the Rockies deserves at least a brief notice. Sperm production takes place during the summer and the bats mate in the fall, yet ovulation does not occur until after the winter has passed. It takes place in late April or early May during transit from the hibernation to summer quarters. The spermatozoa survive the winter in the uterus and fertilize the eggs when they in turn arrive there five or six months later. No doubt, uterine secretions help to keep the sperm alive, but probably the secret here is that the sperm are virtually kept on ice for most of the

211

time. If the temperature of the winter quarters stays between thirty-four and forty degrees above zero the bats go
into a deep sleep, breathing once in five minutes and allow-
ing their own body temperature to drop within a few
degrees of that of the surrounding air. This is cold enough
to immobilize the sperm of any warm-blooded creature—
and the length of life of a spermatozoon depends on how
fast it lives or swims. Without uterine help its energy is
strictly limited, and even before it is completely gone its
power to fertilize an egg usually disappears. The maximum
period that human spermatozoa can survive in the uterus
or oviducts of the female is from two to five days, and the
average time is likely to be much less.

Female mammals, most of them, come into heat at regular
intervals, a succession of events known as the estrus cycles.
The laboratory mouse which breeds throughout the year
passes through such a cycle every five days from the time
it is three months old until senility begins about twelve
months later. The estrus itself, or heat, is usually short.
Even in the elephant it lasts but three or four days, where
it alternates with a long nonsexual season.

A typical cycle begins with the active secretion of the
pituitary hormones that stimulate the growth of the glands,
the ovary in particular, since only the female concerns us
here. This secretion commences either because the animal
has grown to maturity or because of the onset of the breeding season. The ovary enlarges, and the follicle-enclosed
eggs grow rapidly—and, in the follicles, in turn secrete their
particular hormone. The follicles finally burst, releasing both
their own secretion and the eggs.

The period of rapid follicle growth in the ovary of the

212

mouse lasts for about three days; in the human for about two weeks; and during this time the production of the hormone rises to a maximum. It causes the growth and thickening of the uterus and vagina and, simultaneously, changes the whole behavior of the animal so that it becomes eager to mate. This is half the story.

When the follicles rupture and let their contents escape, the empty space fills up with yellow body tissue which produces a hormone of its own. This is the one that prepares the uterus for the reception of the eggs and, at the same time, prevents the pituitary from promoting the growth of any more ovarian follicles. It is a simple, delicate, and exquisite balance of chemical controls, each in a way playing upon the others.

If eggs have been fertilized and pregnancy follows, the yellow bodies of the ovary persist and continue producing their hormone, maintaining a sort of supervisory influence on pregnancy as a whole. The picture, in fact, becomes enormously complex in a chemical way. If, however, there has been no fertilization and no implantation of developing eggs, the yellow bodies fade away, ovarian follicles start up again, and the uterine preparation disappears. In almost all mammals the subsiding of the thickened wall of the uterus takes place imperceptibly, but in old-world monkeys, apes and man the collapse involves actual breakdown of tissue and menstrual bleeding occurs. The difference between our own group and the rest is one of degree only. All mammals show a similar degeneration between successive ovulations and it is a pity that the menstrual cycle has acquired so distinctive a name. The human cycle and that of the Bengal rhesus monkey and the Barbary ape last about twenty-eight days—the lunar month—with variation of a

213

week, more or less. In the gorilla it is forty-five days, the chimpanzee thirty-five, and in the South American capuchin sixteen to twenty days. I doubt that the moon has had much to do with it, although stranger things have happened. At least, the pattern was set a long time ago when our communal ancestors made love among the tree tops—and who knows what effect the moonlight may have had.

These ovarian or estrus cycles make sense, of course, only in relation to pregnancy. They occur during a season that is correlated with the period of gestation, the length of time the egg develops within the womb. The shortest true pregnancy is the sixteen days of the hamster. In mice and rats it is a mere three weeks. And in such animals as these there is time enough for a number of pregnancies each year. The longest pregnancy is the elephant's—twenty-two months. Even the enormously larger whales manage to compress it within a year, giving birth to twenty-foot babies that grow to seventy tons in a couple of years. It is the season of birth that is all-important—to be born in springtime in either the northern or southern hemisphere, no matter what the actual month may be, or in the tropics at any time. Everything conforms to it. Breeding seasons are adjusted so that gestation terminates in spring. The horse breeds in spring and the young are born in spring; roe deer breed in summer and the young are born in spring; the goat breeds in the fall and the young are born in the spring; and the fallow deer breeds in early winter and its young are born in spring. The system is simple—you work backward from the arrival date. Yet when the birth date finally arrives, it is the pituitary gland, as you might expect, that has the last word. It releases another hormone and the milk begins to flow.

214

19. solicitude and power

The milk of human kindness is a phrase of common speech. Do not ever underestimate its meaning. It may have started with a platypus but its end is not in sight, and like so many other things it has a glandular beginning.

Our understanding of the stimulus that causes milk to run is not based on a mammal but on a bird. Pigeons and doves have crop glands in both sexes; both males and females do their part in incubating eggs and feeding young. The lining of pouches of the crop of the birds of each sex thickens during the last half of the incubation period and for the following three weeks thick layers of more or less solid milk are sloughed off into the crop for the nestlings to feed on. Chemically, the crop milk of a dove and mammary milk of a mammal have a good deal in common; anatomically they have none. But it was crop milk that led the way to what we know about it all. A part of the secretion of the dove pituitary was found to be responsible for stimulating the crop to make its milk, but it was a surprise to find that it also stimulated milk production in a mammal. Prolactin is the name for it, which is a narrow one I think, for it brings about not merely the flow of milk but also broodiness, and can cause a virgin rat to cuddle another's young. It has been called the parental hormone. Yet it is not all just chemistry;

the mind is involved as well. A male pigeon, watching his mate with her nestlings, secretes milk into his crop continually, but only so long as he can see what is going on. Hearing alone is not enough. If a board is placed so that he can listen to his family but cannot see it, the milk production stops. When he can see his loved ones once again, the milk is restored. It may, of course, be like the drooling that starts in man and dog at the sight of a juicy piece of steak; or it may be more than that. Birds generally are so flooded with emotion I feel sure there must be a full, rich feeling in a pigeon's throat of which the milk is merely the tangible expression.

Even here it is another case of more or less. In birds as well as in mammals of both sexes, the pituitary gland secretes its prolactin and sex glands form both male and female hormones; but females produce more prolactin and female hormone than the male, and the male produces more male hormone than the female. It is a question of preponderance, although there are more ways than one of weighing down the balance on one side. The stallion, as masculine a male as I have heard of, produces female hormone in enormous quantities from its testes, but the kidneys sift it out into the urine as fast as it is made, in an almost insoluble form, and this is the main commercial source that drug manufacturers employ.

It comes to this, it seems to me, that every warm-blooded individual of either sex, whether it has hair or feathers, has three kinds of hormones—male, female, and broody—circulating within it and each of these influences its behavior in certain ways. Not that these are the only hormones or are by themselves responsible for actions, but they favor this or that kind of action or response. The personality and

216

tendencies of their possessor are strongly influenced by their presence and concentration.

Sex hormones may swing the development of the gland toward ovary or testis if they can exert their influences soon enough, and cause sexual anatomical features to be male or female during later phases of development of the embryo, as we have seen. But when injected into individuals already fully formed, even if not fully grown, the effect upon behavior is startling in its suddenness. Female canaries, injected with male hormone, no longer behave as females, and within a few days sing loud and long in the manner of the male and commence the courtship activities of that sex. Month-old chicks of the black-crowned night heron develop a guttural voice and start defending territories, building nests, courting, mating and brooding. A hen develops a larger comb, takes to crowing and starts to strut.

There is a peck order among hens and other birds and many mammals, and it is hard to know whether to laugh or cry to see a human weakness so widespread within the living world. It is a failing to be deprecated, yet when so many share it we may perhaps find a little comfort, but I fear it means a harder task to throw it off. Among the fowl, the rooster stands at the head of his harem and can peck any individual within the group without being pecked in return. Below him stands a hen who can peck any other hen with impunity, but not the rooster—and so on down the line. Anyone can peck someone lower in the social scale, but it would be an unthinkable error in etiquette to peck one of a higher rank.

It means a lot to be near the top and the more so to be at the peak itself, eating first and mating at pleasure, keeping all others in their place with usually no more than a toss of the head. The pecking order, even in hens, is not always a straight-line system. Pigeons and parakeets have a looser kind, where no one bird wins all the combats but only a majority—power is relative, not absolute. Sex hormones seem to be at the bottom of it, but even here the power is relative and other factors enter in.

When the male sex hormone is injected into low-ranking hens they rise rapidly to the top of the order. There is an increase in general vigor and willingness to fight, and a new level is found and more or less respected by the rest. Only the male hormone produces this effect; what is injected is added to that which the female already has, for we need to remember that the ovary is producing male as well as female hormones in any case. The male hormone becomes the hormone for aggressiveness, and given enough of it, by man or nature, a bird of either sex becomes a bully. The female hormone merely increases female submissiveness and other similar traits.

Hormones are not everything, either in birds or humans. Many a female bird has bettered her social position through male favoritism. A male jackdaw returned to its colony after several months' absence and immediately made himself cock of the rock—and took as his mate a small, social nonentity. The next day, the lady took to bullying the former despot and any others who had too obviously kept her in her place. It is a pity that peronistic situations can arise among birds as well as human beings. The badge of office may be necessary to maintain a social order, but tyranny should always be tempered with a little assassination. This has been said before, but when hormones get out of hand and power for power's sake becomes a lust, displacement is no more than its just reward.

Too much of anything is always harmful, and I doubt that dominance in the world of nature is often carried to the excesses to which we find it among ourselves. One appetite is generally balanced by another. It is surprising what a sudden flush of prolactin can do to a dominant male, although much of this is surmise based on what we know of hens and rats and aquarium fish. You can watch the antics of a tiger and interpret them in terms of glands, but you don't approach a tiger with a hypodermic syringe in your hand. Curiosity can go too far.

In any case, even a crude key that opens a door is better than none at all, and when applied to an ostrich or a pen-

Male ostrich incubating pile of eggs laid by his harem of females.

guin it seems to me that sense is made of actions that have been otherwise hard to understand. For the ostriches of Africa and South America are peculiar in their breeding habits, although peculiarity perhaps applies to all of us in some degree. Male ostriches are both masculine and maternal, females are just female and no more than that. The males have all the aggressiveness of their sex and at the mating season fight it out among themselves, pounding around in an arena with feet and beak in vicious combat. The winner takes all and for the time being has a harem. The losers have to do without, at least in that location. After mating with his group of females, the male makes as much of a nest as an ostrich makes—not much of a one, it is true, but the intention is good. And each female, in the course of a week or so, lays about a dozen enormous eggs within the nest. Thereafter, the male sits in solitude upon them, and any belated eggs a female has are usually dropped where she happens to be. The nest is closed, to be brooded on by the cock for six or seven weeks. Up to the time of mating, the cocks and hens appear to be typical males and females, acting as though they are governed by male and female hormones. After mating is over, the successful cock behaves as though he has all of the broody parental pituitary hormones the race possesses; the females show little sign of having any.

Penguins—emperor penguins, at least—are somewhat different, and here you can see natural selection forcing the pace. The emperors breed in the dark and unbelievably cold midwinter on the great ice barrier of Antarctica. They have no enemies but the elements to contend with. Each egg is incubated against the warmth of a bare skin pouch at the base of the belly, and is lifted off the ice on to the feet. It is easy to lay enough eggs; the problem is to keep the eggs and youngsters warm. Male and female are pretty well equated in almost every way except the fundamentals. Being a bird, it is the male that does the courting, but any penguin looks like any other to a penguin, and it is only by offering a pebble or a feather to all and sundry that an ardent male can determine who is who. The lady of his choice is the one who takes his gift. Otherwise, he couldn't even tell her from a male. Yet once the eggs are laid and the more serious business of hatching them arrives, all the breeding males and females take to brooding them. If there are not enough eggs to go around, even a lump of ice or a frozen chick is better than having an empty feeling where an egg is meant to be cuddled. There must be a heavy dosing with prolactin in both sexes. Those that nature does not so well endow with broodiness fail to hatch their eggs and raise their young—at least in numbers large enough to hold a place.

Mammals vary just as much as birds, working the same hormonal system for all it is worth. The male of the mountain lion apparently is all male and must be kept away from his young; his appetite for flesh is not balanced by solicitude. But the wolf and fox are different. The male wolf is paternal as well as masculine, is guardian to his family and trains his offspring in hunting and safe conduct. How much of it is sheer intelligence, how much emotion, how much the brooding hormone comes into play, I do not know; but family ties are strong, and out of sex and a hormone originally concerned with brooding eggs and making milk come social bonds, a more responsive mind and that intense concern that makes the world go round.

What holds for a family holds for a herd, but the larger

221

number of participants leads to more variable situations. Two of them have been watched more carefully than most: the red deer of Scotland and the elephant seals of Guadeloupe, both isolated and protected in their own small corners of this earth. I find their stories engrossing.

The monarch of the forest is a misnomer for a stag. A stag is merely king for a day. It is the hind who rules, as a matriarch, from season to season. The stag is masculine but not paternal; parenthood is female. In red deer, maternal care lasts often into the third year of life of the offspring,

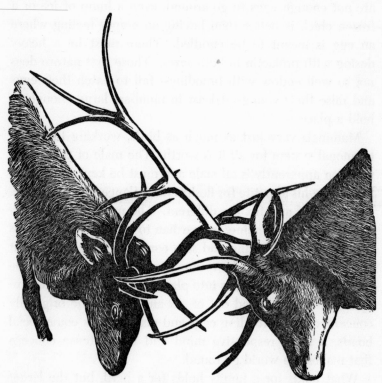

Stags in combat, with clashing antlers.

and it is once again this matter of milk and the solicitude that grows out of it that gives stability to the family and cohesion to the group. The hinds associate and each may have two or three followers, and even some of the adult hinds may be offspring of a hind still within the group. A mature and older hind leads each group of hinds and followers, usually with a calf of her own alongside. She needs to be a breeder, it seems, in order to maintain her leadership. And within such a social group, bound together by milk and maternity for years on end, mutual education and the exercise of intelligence develop as far as the brain of a deer permits them. Yet in interpreting activities we need to remember that a deer and a man are not alike in what the senses mean to them, whatever else there may be in common between two minds. For the most meaningful sense to a deer is smell; then comes hearing, while sight comes after, for vision is color blind and eyes are so placed that while the range is panoramic, there can be little sense of depth. This is not to underestimate the ease with which a deer can detect a movement, even of the eyes of a watcher, but to emphasize the dominance of smell. Sight is used for all that it can tell, but the world within is clearly flooded with aromas.

Milk production lasts throughout the year and this alone denotes continuing formation of pituitary prolactin—and maternal attitudes accompany the milk. The factor here that means so much is continuity; there is no season when the maternal feelings are allowed to lapse. Sociality is the outcome and it feeds upon itself. Milk and hormones flow within the group, no matter how the individual fares, and solicitude goes beyond the immediate blood relationship, as a naturalist in the Sierras discovered. For, while bending

223

over an injured fawn, he looked up to see nine hinds converging on him with anxiety and trepidation mixed together.

There is order within a group of hinds comparable to a peck order without the peck, although in unobtrusive ways, with little female digs, some bickering may go on. The leadership of the dominant hind is subtle but unquestioned, and so is that of the second hind who acts as her assistant—and it has nothing in common with the masculine sort that is the enjoyment of power for its own sake. The leading hind is outstanding in her anxiety for the welfare of the herd, constantly watching, leading the herd when it moves, with the second hind bringing up the rear. And there seems to be a mutual awareness of intent that is difficult to explain.

Within the herd there are families and each family has its leader, but when the families unite for general security or movement, one hind assumes the leadership of the whole. There is no dispute, no pushing up the ladder—seniority in maternity and experience may be most of it, but I doubt it is that alone. The most maternal of the older family matriarchs probably makes her presence felt, and responsibility is easily communicated.

At the time of calving, a pregnant hind goes off on her own and attempts to drive away her youngsters, efforts which mean nothing to the yearling but sends the two- and three-year-olds to a distance. The young hinds rejoin the group of hinds and their own maturing glands merely tie them closer, as their own maternal instincts begin to form. It is the young stag that shows his masculine adolescence in ways that are all too familiar.

For most of the year, the sexes might be different species, the hinds form their matriarchal herd of adult females and juveniles, the stags form companies of their own. Each stag

224

company seems to be a loose aggregation of egocentric males with no acknowledged leader, although any one of the company may throw his weight around to the detriment of the rest. When trouble or the threat of it arises, it is a case of every man for himself, and the one that is farthest off is the first to get away.

Individually, the stag is a wanderer and gets to know a region far beyond his normal territory. The restless independence of the male takes him far afield, and extension of deer territory is the enterprise of stags.

Only in the rutting season do the sexes come together. The matriarchal hind society does not change but the stags interfere with it. Each stag that comes into rut corrals what

Red Deer stag in rut, bellowing warning or challenge to other males.

225

hinds he can, rounding them up as a collie shepherds sheep, and serves them while he can. His harem is insecure and he may lose his hinds at any time to another stag. His only concern is sexual and, if the group should be disturbed, the leading hind assumes responsibility and leads the way to safety. The noble stag just trots along or dashes away on his own. He is male and nothing more.

I cannot visualize a stag without seeing antlers, and antlers are a puzzle. All deer, whether they go by that name or as elk or moose, reindeer or caribou, grow antlers; but only in the last two are they carried by females as well as males. And whether they are carried by both sexes or by the male alone, they are shed every year and regrown. In red deer the antlers grow or regrow in late spring and through the summer, covered by their soft velvet coat of lining tissue. In the fall the velvet sloughs, the antlers harden. The stag's neck thickens and the mane grows long. The testes reach their seasonal maturity, and the roaring of the stag in rut is heard through the woods before the winter starts. The antlers are shed in April and a new set starts to grow at once—although what I think is more than likely is that the old ones are shed because the new ones have started beneath their base, like the displacement of teeth in our childhood.

The linkage with sex glands is definite, though by no means simple. If the testes are damaged or removed during the regrowth of the antlers, growth stops at that point and the velvet is never sloughed for the rest of the animal's life. Moreover, injury to one testis results in defective growth of the antler on the opposite side the following year,—a phenomenon which is even harder to understand.

All reindeer have antlers including does and even fawns.

226

Buck reindeer rut in autumn like the stag, but shed their antlers immediately the rutting season is over. If they are castrated in August when the velvet has been sloughed and antlers already hard, they are shed at once. But does shed their antlers in April or May, a few days after the birth of the fawn. Yet I believe we can make some sense of it if we tie up the growth of antlers with the male sex hormone. It is pure speculation, plausible but unproved, and is as much a pastime as any other—like making pictures out of pieces of a puzzle. One set of facts concerns the growing and the shedding of the antlers in relation to the hormones; another is the use to which they are put; and a third, the manner of their growth.

We start with an assumption that a pair of simple horns was the original and basic defensive equipment of all cloven-hooved vegetarians of either sex. Their possession has become more and more linked with the male sex because the male, by virtue of his hormones, is instinctively the better fighter of the two. But some sort of defense against preying carnivora has been necessary all along. Now there is one thing a race of vegetarians can do with advantage, in the course of many generations, which a carnivorous hunter cannot, and that is to grow to a large size. Large size by itself confers a great deal of protection upon its owner, and when feet are shod and cloven they are effective weapons in themselves. The hunters cannot afford to grow so big—they would lose too much speed and need too much food. And the outcome is that the once essential horns become less necessary than they used to be, and, so to speak, are loosened up for use in other ways.

Antlers seem to be horns that have got out of hand and, as fighting tools, are not so good as simpler kinds. For wood-

227

land creatures they may even be a nuisance. They can be put to a use, but just how useful are they? They are ornamental to trophy hunters, but they are not ornamental objects of sex appeal to hinds. Of this we're sure. You wonder if utility has much to do with it. In any case, there is a theory that regards the excessive size and complexity of antlers as something accidental, of not much use but tolerated for other reasons. It is the same perhaps as the lobster's claws, a form of relative growth. For a lobster's claws grow at a faster rate than does a lobster's body, and the larger the lobster, even larger do the claws become until they can outweigh the body, two to one. This is carrying things much too far but results from the nature of growth itself. And the suggestion has been made, plausibly I think, that antlers grow overlarge and unnecessarily subdivided simply because the animal that grows them has itself grown beyond a certain size. The advantage in having a larger body outweighs the handicap of antlers.

This is clearly only a part of it, for while antlers in their nature go beyond defense requirements, they are not exactly pointless. They come into their own in settling issues between the rutting males. Sometimes, as in caribou, much damage is done in combat; all too often horns are locked and their owners starve to death. In red deer, their absence may be advantageous, for the so-called hummel, which are occasional males that grow no antlers, seems to be more successful in the skirmishes than most; a hard butt from a hard head appears to be disconcerting. Perhaps this account of elks tells the story better. A bull, by blandishment or coercion, had collected a dozen cows, all that he could hold together as a harem. When he brought in any more, he lost some of those that were there before. Then one night at dusk a challenge like a bugle call came from the near-by

228

spruce and he trotted off to meet it. The two bulls, the challenged and the challenger, walked into the meadow to come face to face. The mane of each stood up, their swollen necks throbbed and their antlers clashed. With no more than a couple of shoves the defender broke away and galloped off and the newcomer took over the harem. The hinds couldn't have cared less. This may be the answer. Antlers have nothing to do with courting; in fact, the color-blind mammals do no serious courting of any kind, and what little is done is usually by the female who may at times nuzzle up to the male, but that is all. The mane and the swollen neck, the huge branching antlers that clash discordantly when they meet another's, and the roaring challenge, all add up, it seems to me, to bluff and intimidation. The strength of the opponent is measured by his display, and discretion seems to be the better part of valor. So, perhaps antlers grow to the extent they do simply as an added threat to other males; grow when the sex glands grow, and fall off when they wane; and grow in female caribou and reindeer perhaps because all females produce male hormones as well as female ones, and these animals may have more than most.

Masculinity by itself becomes power without solicitude in the case of mammals. Bullies and tyrants are an affliction in our own societies. They are organized more effectively among elephant seals and others.

Seals have had a lot of publicity and the beach masters of the Alaskan fur seal colonies are pretty well known. The same sort of arrangements holds for the elephant seals, and those of Guadeloupe Island off the coast of the Californian peninsula deserve our close attention in more ways than one. Elephant seal colonies used to be common along the

229

Californian coast for a thousand miles, from somewhere north of San Francisco south to Magdalena Bay. Commercial hunters in the nineteenth century virtually extinguished them, and at the beginning of the present century only a small herd on Guadeloupe Island remained of all the elephant seals of the northern species. It has been touch and go until recently whether even this group would survive, but now there is hope of a healthy recovery and perhaps we can rub one name at least from the list of murdered or probably murdered species.

A colony of animals not too numerous, breeding on a small well-guarded island, who individually have no fear of man whatever, can be studied more intimately than almost any other kind, and full advantage has been taken of the opportunity, for the seals might well be in a zoo. They are worth more than a little thought.

Like any other animal a seal is limited by its structure and the place in which it lives and breeds; and elephant seals perhaps more than most are adapted to the water. They flop and drag themselves around on land with difficulty, and are nearsighted out of water. In the water they are graceful, and even the largest bulls can make ten or twelve miles an hour. When sex is out of season, both males and females appear to go their solitary ways as individuals, fishing to considerable depths and watching out for killer whales. On shore they crowd together with a gregariousness so intense that their bodies lie in contact; none can change its posture without disturbing several, and each tries to hold its place within the herd.

The difference between the sexes is more exaggerated in elephant seals than in any other kind. Females are like most seals, though a little on the large size, generally about ten feet long; but males reach fifteen feet in length, may weigh

230

five thousand pounds, and have a snout which can be in-flated like an elongated balloon. The testes begin to enlarge in the fall, and by January the hormone level reaches the threshold where sexual activity begins; it falls off sharply in March and all is quiet till the season starts again. Fe-males carry their young within the womb for about eleven months, give birth to them in December, and come into heat in January while the pup is still suckling. This is fairly typical of seals in general. All reproductive activities, both rearing young and mating, which take place on shore, are compressed into as short a time as possible.

The pregnant females are the first to come to the beach, where they form compact groups in which they bear their young. Potent males are with them from the start and in-crease in numbers as time goes on. And before very long a typical breeding colony is well established. Its organization is simple but effective.

Dominant bulls space themselves at regular intervals throughout the extended group of females stretched along the beach. Sexually potent but subordinate males form a ring around the whole, waiting for their chance. Non-breeding or juvenile males keep entirely away and show no interest in the proceedings whatsoever. The system funda-mentally is not unlike the deer's, with beach and water re-placing woods and meadow. A female seal shows great solicitude for its own particular offspring, but mild antipathy for other females and other young. The community of ma-ternity, so striking in the hinds, is lacking here. Yet her attitude toward a male is much the same; when in heat she welcomes any male, it matters not which one it is.

A stag corrals his hinds into a harem by running around and jabbing with his antlers. A seal can do nothing of the sort; galumphing about at five miles an hour is no way to hold a bevy of the lighter sex together. The females set the stage, clustering together on the beach whether males are there or not. They will receive any male who can reach them, so it is accordingly up to the males to work things out among themselves, which is what they do. Each male who can sits on a favorable spot and mates with all the females in the area immediately around him. Those females on the fringe care nothing whether they are in this circle or that. Somewhere in this situation it seems to me that masculinity gets its own reward in a somewhat ironic way. There is no harem here in the usual meaning of the word. A male dominates a certain area only in the sense that he can keep away the other males. The females just sit around and suckle their young and await events; what sublimity there is is theirs, and only the males appear ridiculous. For every male is torn between two conflicting purposes—mating with any and all the females he is able to, and driving off or defending himself against other males. It is difficult to do two different things at once successfully.

A big bull keeps other males away by sheer weight and fighting power. He blows his horn with a roaring snort, the snout inflating and vibrating against the roof of his mouth as the air is driven up. The noise comes from the nose and lips, not the voice at all—far better than anything the Bronx has ever made. If the offending male fails to run at once, the bull charges, often leaving a wake of somewhat injured females and squashed youngsters behind him.

The breeding male has a one-track mind, with only two alternatives to take—and his enormous size and ugly snout are the outcome of competitive selection among his sex, of little advantage to the species except in so far as it maintains a quality of vigor. Subordinate males keep to the outskirts and take what comes their way, occasionally making

232

*Elephant seal males challenging
each other with roar from inflated
nose.*

forays when a master seems to be asleep or otherwise engaged. It is then that trouble usually arises, although one
toot of the horn is generally enough to cause retreat. The
threat that lies behind it is no bluff, for every male in a
dominant position had to establish his right through prolonged and bloody battles with contestants. He knows his
strength and is only too ready to use it; and his superiority
usually can be seen in the virtual absence of wounds and
scars on a dominant bull, while most of the subordinate
competitors show large fresh wounds through the breeding
season. The challenges are frequent and a beach master
dares not leave his post to search for food. The position is
no sinecure.

A harem master, in fact, rarely if ever makes any attempt
to prevent a female leaving his territory. All his efforts are
directed toward keeping other males away, and mating with
a female is, as much as anything else, a sexual flourish that

emphasizes his mastery of the situation. A single case report shows the strain he is under. A female left a herd and headed for the sea. As soon as she entered the water, five subordinate males hovering outside the surf converged upon her under forced draft, then reared and blew their horns in an effort to drive one another off by vocal challenge alone. The noise attracted the harem master who, without taking time to send a warning blast, charged full speed down the beach toward the turmoil in the water. The subordinates all drew off without a gesture and the harem bull caught up with the female and mated with her.

When the cat's away the mice will play—and during the interlude in the water four ever-ready subordinate males moved into the beach territory temporarily abandoned by its master. All four at once engaged in a frenzy of fighting, vocalizing and attempts to mate with females. As soon as one would pin a female down, another male would interrupt with a bite or a threat, and a four-way running battle went on for twenty minutes without sexual satisfaction to anyone. Then, as if by mutual agreement, all settled down to sleep among the females. Even this was interrupted, for the harem master finally returned and protested loudly, causing them to wake and quietly go away, leaving the almighty one to go to sleep in turn. Dominance and nothing less will do. The mighty male, with little thought of anything but throwing his weight around, rules the roost, and it seems that maleness undiluted is too often sound and fury, signifying little more than nothing. It makes the males of sea elephants into overgrown monstrosities, and I doubt that the benefits to the race are very real. Lust and power need seasoning with solicitude, lest the salt shall lose his savor.

234

20. the garden of eden

If man is a mammal he is also a primate, and an anthropoid at that; which puts him in his place with a vengeance. How closely he belongs there is a matter of opinion, but anatomically he stays there with the rest. Otherwise, structure has no meaning and the mouse is no kin to the rat; nor the tortoise to the turtle, nor the hare to the rabbit, nor the monkey to the ape; neither can you laugh when you see a chimpanzee—for laughter admits the caricature. Smile at it if you like, as though it were a child, and the ape may grin back at you—and that is something else.

Whether we look to the apes and monkeys or look to ourselves, we find our own distinctive nature emerging in the tree tops—all trapeze work in gymnasiums is nostalgic exercise. But no matter what the details of our emergence from the mammals as a whole, we and the lesser folk that bother some of us so much took to living in the trees at a very early stage. This may not seem to have much connection with sex or reproduction, but it has its bearing and I think is all-important.

What any animal can do or be depends very much on where it lives. And putting it as briefly as I can, tree life converted running feet into grasping hands, and brought

235

eyes to the front for stereoscopic vision so that distances to be jumped could be estimated. The eye and hand relationship was established, from which comes much of the distinctive nature of our brain. The nose was lifted from the ground and the dominating sense of smell became a relic of the past. In the light of the sun and the blaze of color of life in general in the crown of tropical forests, color vision was reacquired or in some way resurrected. Only the primates among all of the mammals are known to see the rainbow, except perhaps the squirrel who more belatedly has made the same arboreal adventure. And last, but by no means least, in marking a path for a future, litters became impossible and only single young were born that could cling to their mother's shoulders. Change any of this and we would never have been. It is our heritage, and much of what we cherish most was made possible by trees. Our capacities and also our limitations have been set by our past, and we need to know them both if we wish to understand ourselves. And if there was ever a miracle, I think it was this: that in a nocturnal class of animals that had lost its sense of color through ages of disuse, one little group that climbed back into the sun was ever able to regain it—for a talent that is buried is rarely given back. Think of this a little when you next see a sunset, or a very pretty vision walking down the street.

There were monkeys of a kind before there were apes, and apes of a kind before there were men, although all that now live have had ample time to become different in many particular ways from what their ancestors used to be. Yet we can, I believe, draw certain conclusions and say for instance that what is common to them all was established in the beginning—such as more or less monthly breeding cycles

236

in the female, involving menstruation at the close of each cycle and ovulation and sexual receptivity in the middle; with the breeding season spread throughout the year, except perhaps in summer heat; and sexual desire greatest in the female at certain times, and not limited to any particular period within the cycle—with males attracted to adult or adolescent females at any time. Hormones undoubtedly continue to play their part, but their control is slipping as the mind begins to dominate. Sexual jealousy may be strongly shown by either sex.

We can also say in all assurance that the kinds of things now eaten by apes and monkeys are the same general sort that were eaten from the first, for teeth can always be relied upon to tell the story. Food, for the most part, consists of fruit of various trees, with grubs and other insects adding some variety. Almost anything is eaten that can be found in safety among the branches. The diet is mainly, though not entirely, vegetarian.

We have more in common with the apes than we have with monkeys, anatomically as well as in other ways—and apart from larger brains and tails that are abortive, apes are individually bigger than the monkey kind and spend more time upon the ground, some of them more than others. Their social unit, which many of the old-world monkeys have as well, is a nonpromiscuous family group held together just as long as its male overlord can hold his females and keep other males away. It is the old familiar pattern on a modest scale. And while hormones are not everything, each female of a harem has her rhythmic sexual peak, when she becomes the favorite wife for the moment; then she yields and another female takes her place. The family group moves

237

along together as it gathers food, still vegetarian but as interested in roots as in higher things.

Such is the background from which we as humans have emerged—not from any kind of ape that we know anything about, but at least from creatures that we would look upon as being much the same, with a vegetarian diet and family groups of a dominant male and several breeding females— with minds too much like our own for comfort and challenging the old hormonal controls.

Our personal human history has been something of a shakedown. Either because our ancestors grew too large or because too many tropical forests disappeared too fast, or a little of each, we in our subhuman beginnings found ourselves back on the ground for good—at least, as far as trees are concerned. Hind feet that had become adapted to hold-

Male, female, and suckling young of the Arabian baboon.

238

ing on to branches had to readjust to walking on the comparatively flat earth, and posture became more upright as bipedal balancing became perfected, with the pelvis spread to give the legs a better gait. Meanwhile, the very changes that brought us down to earth made the customary sort of food-gathering increasingly difficult. With the disappearance of the forests from wide extents of the earth went the fruits of the forest and the roots and plants that they sheltered. Habits had to change and we are evidence that they did. At some stage in the making of a man he took to hunting animals as well as digging roots. He became omnivorous, ready and able to eat almost anything he could find, developing a catholicity of taste that made survival possible and has left us with an appetite that no one else possesses. For the rule has always been "adapt or disappear."

You cannot change your way of life in any fundamental manner without having to make other changes, too. And it is easy to get the picture of the situations which arose. One man, or whatever we may call him, with several wives and a larger number of children, could not stalk game of any kind if he had to take the family along. In order to get meat he would have to hunt alone, except perhaps for other males, and leave his womenfolk and children at home to collect what roots and fruit they could. Under circumstances such as these the old system wouldn't work. A male that intimidates other males and controls a large family group in the old-fashioned way cannot safely go off hunting and leave it alone. Other males would move in at once when opportunity came. For no matter what the social organization may be, males and females are born in approximately equal numbers, and in the hunting, or mixed hunting and food-gathering economy that early man had to assume, there was

239

no place for a system of dominant males each with a harem of several females, all in the midst of a much larger number of unattached adult males. The larger groups would have to break up into smaller ones of a more equitable kind, or else slowly starve. Gradually, natural selection must have worked on the conflict between polygamous greed and the drive to obtain enough food; monogamy became established as an essential discipline for primitive food-gathering and hunting peoples. The alternative was extinction and this, I imagine, was the fate of most but not of all.

In the end we are thrown back upon the reproductive cells, and the importance of having two cells combine to do the work of one. For eggs and sperm relate to evolution; there have been simpler ways of reproduction when only duplication has been required. Not only do hereditary units within the cells change their nature from time to time, but each cell contains enormous numbers of them, some showing their influence and others not, and in the process of fusion of sperm and eggs all manner of combinations can be made. As long as eggs and spermatozoa play their part, there seems to be no end to the possible recombination of their constituents, no end to variations among the offspring of two parents. Without demanding actual changes other than some reshuffling of what already exists, the chances of two children who are not identical twins, or any two individuals in this world, being exactly alike are about as slim as the chance that one of them one day will spontaneously explode. The number of possible variations among the progeny of humanity is as astronomical as the distance to a star. The never-ending reshuffling of hereditary units that is brought about by the making of eggs and sperm and their subsequent fusion in fertilization, and the occasional real changes that do occur in these units, are the mainspring of evolution. Reproduction by itself can get along without it, but evolutionary change cannot. I doubt that it ever will.

This tendency to vary underlies all that we have concern with. When animals are perfectly adjusted to their circumstances, natural selection favors those that are like their parents. Those that are markedly different are less likely to get along so well, less likely to reach maturity and leave offspring in their turn. Selection can act in a conservative way. On the other hand, it can readily force a change.

Look once again, for a moment, at the elephant seal. Among the progeny of a colony some will grow to a larger and some to a smaller size than the average. In females it may have no significance or may be even a disadvantage; a certain average size typical of seals in general is maintained and circumstances favor the normal more than departures from the normal. In the case of males it is different. When larger size, greater strength and more ferocity enable a male to mate with females, to the exclusion of other males, those characters are more likely to be passed on to the males of the next generation than are those of the males that do not mate or at least do not mate so often. The heavier and more aggressive breeders are favored for generation after generation. The rest fail to produce their kind and the scale is shifted finally about as far as it can go. The male become enormous—in this case a sex-linked character associated with the male combination of hereditary units and not the female assortment. Yet it takes time, and for the male seal to have grown so far beyond the usual size must have taken a very large number of generations. Yet even

241

if the trend started as recently as in the late Pliocene, about five million years ago, there has been time for a million generations to effect it, more than time enough.

So we come, in turn, to our own ancestral transformations. As the large family groups with dominant males progressively found themselves ranging farther and farther in search of food, selection began to operate in the opposite sense from that in the elephant seal, but in relation to food rather than dominance and sexual drive directly. Males that continued to dominate their particular groups might produce more offspring than less aggressive ones, but their young would be much more likely to starve to death. In the long run, the progeny left to carry on the race would be by individuals that were less aggressive; those males who were content with a single female, males whose male hormones were less abundant and better balanced with female hormone and with the parental kind. Males such as these, I believe, were being born all the time, but as long as food was abundant they were not the ones that succeeded in mating and passing on their own particular traits. The variables are always present, and as the wind blows so the sand drifts. And in shifting circumstances, the more adaptable the patterns of behavior the more likely that a new situation will be coped with. Selection continued to loosen the chemical shackles of the mind.

I find it difficult to draw a line between one phase of human evolution and another, though much of it goes far beyond our present reference. Yet so much of our humanity depends on something else than mobile hormones and an astonishing brain; it depends on a peculiarity of development which could have occurred only where one offspring at a time is nourished in the womb. Compared with almost all other kinds of mammals we live for an extraordinary length of time. Our three score years and ten may be matched by an elephant, but I do not know of any other. And it is not just a case of not wearing out; the whole life cycle has been affected. We develop slowly in the womb and grow slowly through childhood; we reach puberty at about fifteen and full growth a little later; we breed effectively for about thirty years and generally live a quarter century longer. But in monkeys, cattle and the greatest whales puberty is reached in two or three years at the most, while at the ripe old age of twenty they are more than likely senile. Our extended age is not something tacked on to maturity—it is as though someone took the beginning and the end of life and stretched the whole. There is, in fact, some truth in saying that we never really grow up but toddle from one childhood to the other, playing at soldiers and with fire and wondering what it is all about. Yet, to a great extent, it is this stretching out of time that makes us human—and with time on our hands and a youthful curiosity, it is no wonder that our minds interfere with the delicate balance of our glands and tend to make us stray from the straight and narrow path. It goes back to the apes, for they also are slow in reaching puberty, have notorious curiosity, and in captivity, at least, are inclined to let sex get out of bounds. It is much too easy to make a monkey out of man and you can readily find a book about it if you want to.

There is a distinctive human trait which is disturbing and is an accidental consequence of another. During the final skeletal adjustment that had to be made in order that we should walk and run upright and well, certain changes came about in hips, leg bones and muscles which set us apart

243

The Vigland circle of life, Oslo, Norway.

from other primates. The consequence was a change in the position assumed for mating, from the almost universal rear approach to sexual union, front to front. This may not seem important enough to emphasize, but it has introduced something new and unexpected. For the first time in fifty or a

244

hundred million years of mammalian history, the male has become able to inflict his will upon the female, whether she shows willingness or not. In all of the mammalian world except the human, the female controls the sexual situation—a male can mate with her when she is good and ready and not at any other time; masculine impatience is kept in its place and in the case of birds the male has more to do than wait and in most cases must attract or stimulate the female with his song and dance. Man alone, in all the living kingdom except for a certain spider, so far as I can tell, is capable of rape. And it is more than an occasional crime of our own civilization. The control of the sexual decision has passed ostensibly from the female to the male, and much of the subordinate position of women has been the result of it. Fear of rape has been paramount in many primitive societies. Among the North American Indians, Australian aborigines, various tribes in Africa and India, solitary unprotected women are or until recently were abused on sight; and out of this general situation many of the curbs on women's freedom and occupations apparently have arisen. Institutions like the purdah of India and Persia are primarily protective; while child marriage, common in India and in aboriginal Australia, which sanctions the physical injury of small girls by grown men, is a social exploitation of a human male prerogative.

So here we stand—free of the old restraints—influenced by hormones but not controlled by them, free from the bonds of a breeding season, conscious of sight above all else; using the symbolic processes our minds have developed to reach out and master the external world. Yet our new freedom, which in terms of evolutionary time is no older than yesterday, brings disadvantage with it. For, so far, we have failed to agree about the shape that human relationships should take. This has to be settled, just as the social change from the older system had to be made one or two million years ago. But it leaves us in the midst of violent intraspecific and internecine struggles that have no end in sight. We are born into a world of tensions and, while the form of them will change, I doubt that the kind of quiet and restful peace most of us desire will ever come.

There is another side to it. We are using our minds to explore our beginnings, delving into heredity and hormones and history to the limit of our ingenuity, trying to find our future pathway by tracing the way we have come—and writing books about it all, sex especially.

Yet out of sex cells came evolution; from sex hormones came the sexes and a certain mutual bondage; from milk came maternity and the concern of parenthood in general; climbing a tree brought color, a hand, and a mind—and something of a voice; and on descending, we find ourselves endowed with a mixture of unwanted heritage and the beginnings of spiritual grace. We start with life and sex, and we are left with love and a mind with an eye for beauty. Where we go from here, I do not know.

book list

The following is a list of books which I have had occasion to consult in connection with the foregoing discussion. Those that have appealed to me more than others are starred with an asterisk. The many articles in special journals that have been an inevitable part of my own reading I have not included since they are not generally accessible.

ALLEN, E. (edit.) *Sex and internal secretions.* Williams and Wilkins Co., Baltimore, Md. 1939.

*ARMSTRONG, E. A. *Bird display and behaviour.* Lindsay Drummond. London. 1947.

ASDELL, S. A. *Patterns of mammalian reproduction.* Comstock Publishing Co. Ithaca, N. Y. 1946.

BARTHOLOMEW, G. A. *Reproductive and social behavior of the northern Elephant Seal.* Univ. California Press (Publ. in Zoology) Berkeley, Calif. 1952.

BEACH, F. A. *Sexual behavior in animals and men.* The Harvey Lectures 1947-8. The Science Press. 1950.

BEACH, F. A. *Hormones and behavior.* Paul B. Hoeber. N. Y. 1948.

BRISTOWE, W. S. *A comity of spiders.* Ray Society. London. 1941.

*BULLOUGH, W. S. *Vertebrate sexual cycles.* Methuen. London. 1951.

BURRELL, H. The platypus. Sidney, Australia. 1927.

BURROWS, H. *Biological actions of sex hormones.* Cambridge Univ. Press. N. Y. 1945.

*CAHALANE, V. H. *Mammals of North America.* Macmillan Co. N. Y. 1947.

COLE, F. J. *Early theories of sexual generation.* Oxford Univ. Press. N. Y. 1930.

COOK, R. C. *Human fertility: The modern dilemma.* Sloane Associates. N. Y. 1951.

*CORNER, G. W. *The hormones in human reproduction.* Princeton Univ. Press. Princeton, N. J. 1947.

CORNER, G. W. *Ourselves unborn.* Yale Univ. Press. New Haven, Conn. 1944.

*DARLING, FRASER. *A herd of Red deer.* Oxford Univ. Press. N. Y. 1937.

DARLING, FRASER. *Bird flocks and breeding cycles.* Cambridge Univ. Press. N. Y. 1938.

DARWIN, C. *The effects of cross- and self-fertilization in the vegetable kingdom.* Murray. London. 1876.

247

SEX AND THE NATURE OF THINGS

DARWIN, C. *The different forms of flowers in plants of the same species.* Murray. London. 1877.

FARRIS, E. J. *Human fertility and problems of the male.* Author's Press. N. Y. 1950.

FISHER, J. *Birds as animals.* Heinemann. London. 1940.

FORD, E. B. *Butterflies.* Collins. London. 1945.

FRASER, J. G. *The Golden Bough.* Macmillan. N. Y. 1941.

GOLDSCHMIDT, R. *The mechanism and physiology of sex determination.* Methuen. London. 1923.

HOOTON, E. A. *Up from the Ape.* Macmillan. N. Y. 1946.

*HOWARD, E. *A waterhen's world.* Cambridge Univ. Press. N. Y. 1940.

*HUXLEY, J. S. *Evolution in action.* Harper. N. Y. 1952.

IMMS, A. D. *Insect natural history.* Collins. London. 1947.

KOCH, F. C. AND D. E. SMITH (edit.) *Sex hormones.* (Biological Symposium IX). The Jaques Cattell Press. N. Y. 1942.

*LEVICK, G. M. *Antarctic Penguins: a study of their social habits.* Heinemann. London.

LILLIE, F. R. *Problems of fertilization.* Chicago Univ. Press. Chicago, Ill. 1918.

*LORENZ, K. Z. *King Solomon's Ring.* Methuen. London. 1952.

MEYER, A. W. *The rise of embryology.* Stanford Univ. Press. Stanford, Calif. 1939.

*NOBLE, RUTH C. *The nature of the beast.* Doubleday. N. Y. 1945.

PLATT, A. *The love of the Lyre Bird.* Robertson and Mullens. Melbourne. 1946.

*PLATT, RUTHERFORD. *This green world.* Dodd, Mead & Co. N. Y. 1942.

SCHEINFELD, A. *The new You and Heredity.* Lippincott. Philadelphia, Pa. 1950.

SEWARD, G. H. *Sex and the social order.* McGraw-Hill. N. Y. 1946.

STONOR, C. R. *Courtship and display among birds.* Country Life Press. Garden City, N. Y. 1940.

WALLS, G. L. *The vertebrate eye.* Cranbrook Institute of Science. Bloomfield, Mich. 1942.

YERKES, R. M. AND A. W. *The great apes.* Yale Univ. Press. New Haven, Conn. 1929.

YERKES, R. M. AND A. W. *Chimpanzees: a laboratory colony.* Yale Univ. Press. New Haven, Conn. 1943.

ZUCKERMAN, S. *The social life of monkeys and apes.* London. 1932.

248

index

249